LANGUAGE ARTS

WILLIAM & MARY

THE CENTER FOR GIFTED EDUCATION

Literary Reflections

Second Edition

Student Guide

Grades 4-5

Kendall Hunt
publishing company

Kendall Hunt
publishing company

www.kendallhunt.com
Send all inquiries to:
4050 Westmark Drive
Dubuque, IA 52004-1840
1-800-542-6657

Center for Gifted Education
College of William & Mary
PO Box 8795
Williamsburg, VA 23187-8795
757-221-2362
www.cfge.wm.edu

Funded by the Jacob K. Javits Program, United States Department of Education, under a subcontract
from the Washington-Saratoga-Warren-Hamilton-Essex BOCES, Saratoga Springs, New York.

Printed by: Lisghtning Source
United States of America
Batch number: 426496

Printed in the United States of America

Contents

Letter to Student

Dear Student:

You are participating in a special language arts unit called *Literary Reflections.* It is organized around the concept of change and has many activities designed to help you understand this concept.

A wide variety of literature will allow you to explore the concept of change. The literature will stimulate discussion, writing, listening, vocabulary study, and research activities. In class, we will read and discuss short pieces of literature: poems, short stories, and folktales. You will also read two novels. To clarify your thinking and to help you prepare for written and oral assignments, you will keep a journal. As you read the literature, you will respond to it and think critically about it by analyzing ideas, vocabulary, and structure.

The purpose of this book is to provide you with additional materials that you will need to participate in the unit. All of the shorter unit readings are contained in this book, as well as Activity Pages related to all literature selections.

During the course of the unit, you will be using several models to help organize your thinking. They include:

1. Literature Web Model
2. Vocabulary Web Model
3. Hamburger Model for Persuasive Writing
4. Reasoning Model (including the Reasoning About a Situation or Event Model)
5. Writing Process Model
6. Research Model

An explanation of these models is included on pages 5–16. Your teacher will also explain how these models work so that you can use them as you read the unit literature and complete the required activities.

Sincerely,

Curriculum Development Team
Center for Gifted Education at The College of William & Mary

Glossary of Literary Terms

The following literary terms may be useful in understanding the discussion of literature within this unit.

Allegory: a narrative that is an extended metaphor. In an allegory, the characters, setting, and other parts of the story have both literal and symbolic meanings.

Alliteration: the repetition of consonant sounds at the beginning of words or stressed syllables. A poet may use alliteration to dramatize action or mimic actual sounds.

Character: a person portrayed in a story or drama. Characters can be unique or stereotypical.

Climax: the decisive moment of a narrative or drama, usually the most intense part of the story and occurring near the end.

Denouement: the resolution of a narrative or drama, following the climax.

Dialogue: the conversation between characters in a narrative or drama.

Figurative language: language that is not literal. Similes, metaphors, and personification are examples of figurative language. They represent something through a direct or implied comparison with something else.

Free verse: verse with no meter, variable line length, and either no rhyme or an unpatterned use of rhyme.

Imagery: the use of language to create vivid sensory impressions in the imagination.

Metaphor: a type of figurative language in which two unlike things are compared; in a metaphor, one thing is said *to be* the other; for example, *The girl is a ray of sunshine.*

Motivation: the desire or reasons that drive a character to act.

Narrative: a story or account telling about events that may be fictional or true.

Narrator: the person who tells a story; the voice that an author employs to tell a story.

Personification: a type of figurative language in which animals, objects, or ideas take on human characteristics.

Plot: the series of events that make up a story.

Point of view: the position from which a narrator tells a story, either within the story (first person) or as an outside observer (third person).

Protagonist: the main character.

Setting: the time, place, and circumstances in which a story takes place.

Simile: a type of figurative language in which two unlike things are compared using the words *like* or *as;* for example, *Her mind was as sharp as a blade.*

Stanza: a grouping of lines of verse within a song or poem.

Structure: the order of the parts of a story or poem, and the relationship of the parts to each other and to the work as a whole.

Symbol: an image, word, or object that stands for something greater than itself; the image is usually visible, but what it represents is often invisible. For example, the flag is a symbol of patriotism.

Theme: the central idea of a poem, short story, or novel.

Voice: the tone, attitude, or personality of the speaker as it reveals itself directly or indirectly in the narrative.

Models

The following pages include information about some models that you can use to help organize your thinking.

The Literature Web Model

The Literature Web is designed to guide you in interpreting your reading by helping you connect your personal response with elements of the text. The web may also be used as a tool for discussion. The kinds of observations that belong in each of the five parts of the web are as follows:

1. *Key words:* interesting, unfamiliar, striking, or important words and phrases within the text

2. *Feelings:* your feelings and the specific text details that inspire them; the characters' feelings; and the feelings that you infer the author intended to inspire

3. *Ideas:* major themes and main ideas of the text; key concepts

4. *Images and symbols:* notable sensory images in the text; "pictures" the text creates in your mind and the details that inspire them; symbols for abstract ideas

5. *Structure:* the formal elements of the writing and their contribution to meaning; including such things as time order, comparison, cause/effect, spatial order, use of voice, use of figurative language, and repetition

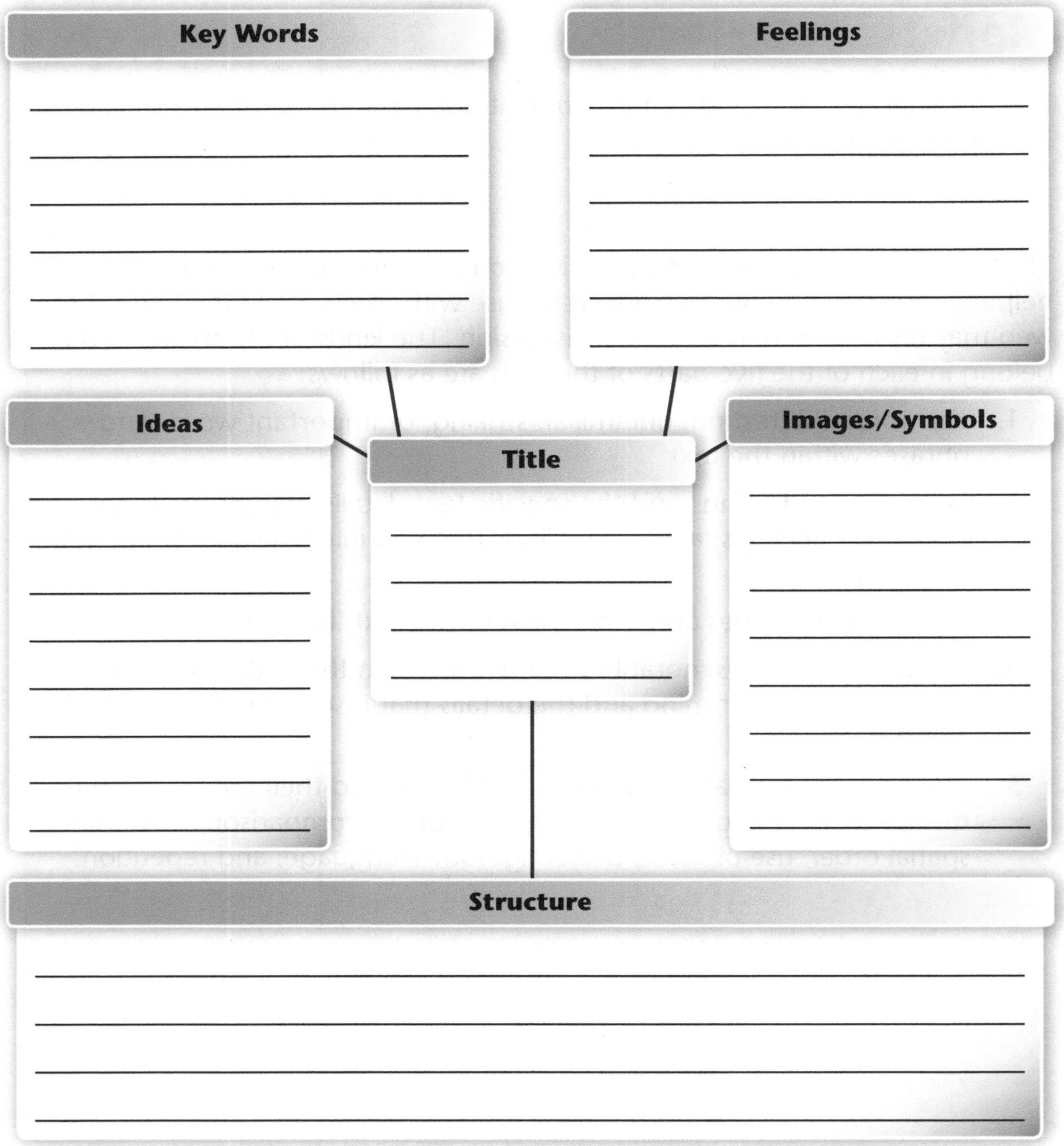

Key Words

_____
_____
_____
_____
_____

Feelings

_____
_____
_____
_____
_____

Ideas

_____
_____
_____
_____
_____
_____
_____

Title

_____
_____
_____
_____

Images/Symbols

_____
_____
_____
_____
_____
_____
_____

Structure

_____
_____
_____
_____

Figure 1-1: Literature Web Model

The Vocabulary Web Model

The Vocabulary Web is a tool for exploring a word in depth. Find the definition of the word and its part of speech, synonyms and antonyms, word stems, and origin. For word families, try to find at least three other words that use one or more of your word's stems. Then create an example to explain your word (a sentence, an analogy, a picture or diagram, etc.). Use the Vocabulary Web to organize your responses.

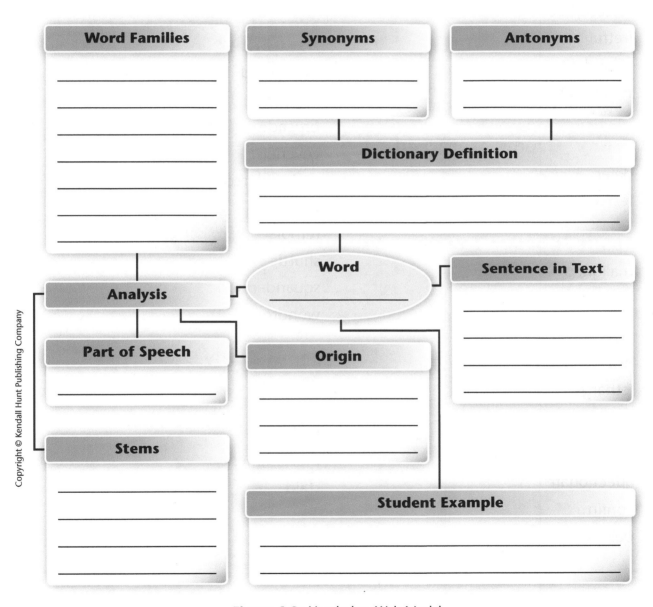

Figure 1-2: Vocabulary Web Model

Unit vocabulary words you may want to explore include:

From *The Secret Garden**:

affectionate

bewilderment

desolate

discomfited

fretful

impudent

tyrannical

*Not a complete vocabulary list.

From "Dream Deferred":

defer

fester

From "Border Towns":

maligned

From "The Habit of Movement":

dispossession

lethargy

From "The Old Man and His Affectionate Son":

affectionate

confirm

delicacy

discard

remarkable

sagacious

succession

From *The Weaving of a Dream*:

astonished

beggar

brocade

coverlet

embroidered

plead

remorse

shuttle

squandering

wondrous

From Emily Dickinson poems:

alabaster

indicative

presentiment

staid

The Hamburger Model for Persuasive Writing

The Hamburger Model uses a sandwich as a metaphor to help you construct a paragraph or essay. Begin by stating your point of view on the issue in question (the top bun). Then provide reasons, or evidence, to support your claim; you should try to incorporate at least three supporting reasons (the "patties"). Elaboration on the reasons provides additional details (the "fixings"). A concluding sentence or paragraph wraps up the piece of writing (the bottom bun).

Figure 1-3: Hamburger Model for Persuasive Writing

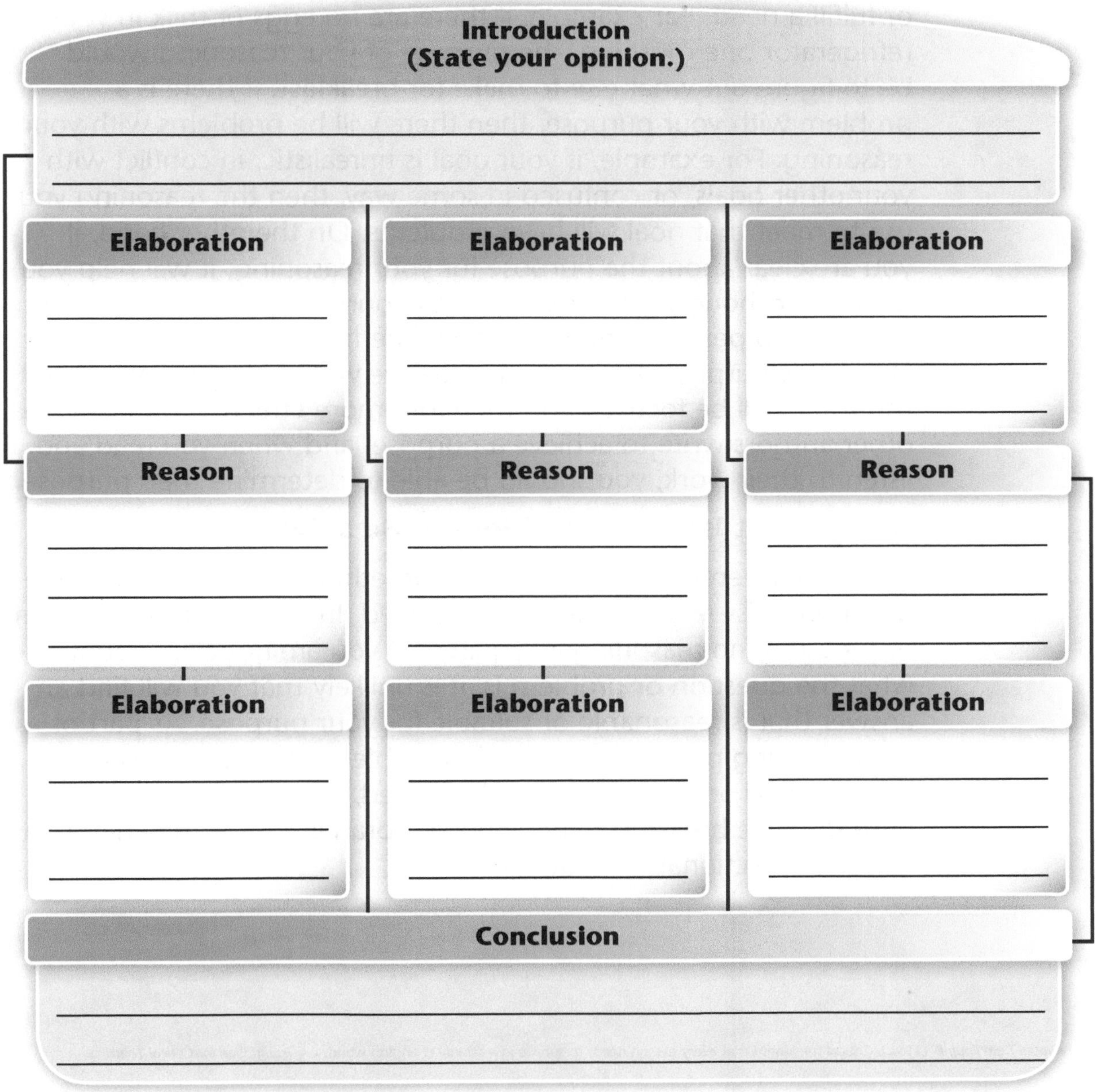

**Introduction
(State your opinion.)**

Elaboration	Elaboration	Elaboration
Reason	Reason	Reason
Elaboration	Elaboration	Elaboration

Conclusion

The Reasoning Model

In the Elements of Reasoning (1992), the theorist Richard Paul provides a model of critical thinking. The model breaks down the thinking process into eight elements, or parts. Use the model and the following terms to help you think about issues and problems.

The eight Elements of Reasoning are as follows:

1. **Purpose, Goal, or End View**

   We reason for a purpose—to achieve an objective, satisfy a desire, or fulfill a need. For example, if there are no eggs or milk in your refrigerator one morning, the purpose of your reasoning would be to figure out what else to make for breakfast. If there is a problem with your purpose, then there will be problems with your reasoning. For example, if your goal is unrealistic, in conflict with your other goals, or confused in some way, then the reasoning you use to meet that goal will have problems. On the other hand, if you are clear about the purpose for your reasoning, it will help you focus your thoughts. For example, the purpose of your reasoning might be to persuade others to do something. If you are clear about this purpose, then your persuasive writing and speaking on this topic will be focused and therefore more effective. Similarly, other authors write to achieve a purpose, and when you read and listen to their work, you should be able to determine their purpose.

2. **Question at Issue (or Problem to Be Solved)**

   When we attempt to reason about something, there is at least one question at issue or problem to be solved. In fact, without question or problem, no reasoning is required! If you are not clear about what the question or problem is, it is unlikely that you will find an answer that is reasonable or suitable for your purpose. As part of the reasoning process, you should be able to state the question to be answered or the problem to be solved, such as, "What else can I use to make breakfast?" or, "Should libraries censor materials that contain objectionable language?"

Copyright © Kendall Hunt Publishing Company

Adapted from Paul, R. (1992). Critical thinking: What every person needs to survive in a rapidly changing world. CA: Foundation for Critical Thinking.

3. **Point of View or Frame of Reference**

As we reason about an issue, we are influenced by our own point of view. For example, parents of young children and librarians might have different points of view about censorship. Another example is that the price of a shirt may seem low to one person and high to another, depending on their frame of reference. Any problem in your point of view or frame of reference is a possible source of problems in your reasoning. Your point of view may be too narrow, not precise enough, or biased. By considering multiple points of view, you can sharpen or broaden your thinking. Similarly, in writing and speaking, you can strengthen your argument by acknowledging other points of view. In listening and reading, you need to identify the perspective of the speaker or author and understand how it affects the message.

4. **Experiences, Data, Evidence**

When we reason, we must be able to support our point of view with evidence. The use of evidence, including data from surveys or published studies, helps you to distinguish reasons from opinions, make well-reasoned judgments, and strengthen your arguments. In reading and listening, you can evaluate the strength of an argument or the validity of a statement by examining the supporting data or evidence. Experience can also provide evidence or data. For example, previous experiences making breakfast might contribute to the process of figuring out what to make for breakfast.

5. **Concepts and Ideas**

Reasoning requires the understanding and use of concepts and ideas, including definitional terms, principles, rules, or theories. When you read or listen, you can ask yourself, "What key ideas are being presented?" When you write or speak, you can examine and organize your thoughts around concepts and ideas. Some examples of concepts are freedom, friendship, and responsibility.

6. Assumptions

Although we may need to take some things for granted when we reason, we need to be aware of the assumptions we have made and the assumptions of others. As a writer or speaker, you make assumptions about your audience and message, and faulty assumptions can lead to problems in your reasoning. For example, you might assume that others will share your point of view, or you might refer to "First Amendment rights" without any explanation because you incorrectly assume that your audience is familiar with the First Amendment. As a reader or listener, you should be able to identify the assumptions of the writer or speaker.

7. Inferences

Reasoning proceeds by small mental steps called inferences. An inference is a conclusion that something is true because something else is true, or seems to be true. The inferences you make depend on the data you have and your assumptions. For example, if you see dark clouds, you might infer that it is going to rain. Or if it is now 6:45 and it takes 30 minutes to get to the movie theater, you will probably conclude that you cannot get to the theater in time for a 7:00 movie. Many inferences are justified and reasonable, but many are not. You need to distinguish between the raw data of your experiences and your inferences about those experiences. Also, be aware that the inferences you make are heavily influenced by your point of view and assumptions.

8. Implications and Consequences

When your reasoning takes you in a certain direction, you need to look at the implications of following that line of reasoning. When you support a certain point of view, for example, solid reasoning requires that you consider what the consequences might be of taking the course that you support. Similarly, when you read or listen to an argument, you need to ask yourself what follows from that way of thinking. You can also consider consequences of actions that characters in stories take, just as you can consider consequences of your own actions. For example, if you don't do your homework, then you might have to stay after school to complete it; or, if you water your lawn, it may not wither in the summer heat.

Figure 1-4: Wheel of Reasoning

Assumptions	**Data, Evidence**
What assumptions does the author make about the concept of change?	What evidence is presented that the central character is motivated by a given emotion?

Issue	**Concept**
What is the central issue of this story?	What concepts are central to understanding the story? What do we understand about these concepts?

Reasoning in Literature

Implications	**Point of View**
What are the implications of character behavior at this point in the story?	From what point of view is the story written?

Purpose	**Inferences**
What is the purpose of the poem/story?	What inferences might be made about the ending of the story based on specific events?

The Writing Process Model

The writing process describes the stages that writers go through to develop a written composition. The stages are not separate parts that writers go through from one to five; rather, writers move back and forth among the stages and use them to construct, clarify, and polish their writing. The Writing Process Model is used throughout the unit to encourage you to engage in improving your writing.

The following are the stages of the writing process:

1. *Prewriting:* List your ideas and begin to organize them. You may want to use a graphic organizer such as a web or Venn diagram. Graphic organizers help you to "see" what you will write about. As you write, you can add to your graphic organizer or change it.

2. *Drafting:* Write a rough draft, getting your ideas onto paper and not worrying about mechanics such as spelling, grammar, or punctuation. Some writers call this stage "composing." Sometimes this stage is a "messing around" stage in which your drafting or composing helps you to "hear" what you want to say.

3. *Revising:* Conferencing is an essential step in the revising stage. Ask people (friends, family, teachers) to read and listen to your work and to tell you what they like, what they'd like to know more about, and what they don't understand. This is the place to make major changes in your draft. Sometimes you may want to go back to the prewriting stage and redo your graphic organizer to give your paper a new structure.

4. *Editing:* After you have revised your paper, look for the small changes that will make a big difference. Check your choice of words and identify mechanical errors. After you make the changes and corrections, proofread your work one final time. You may want to ask a friend or an adult for help.

5. *Sharing or publishing:* There are numerous ways to share and to publish your work. You can bind it into a book, copy it in your best handwriting and post it on a bulletin board, read it aloud to your class or family, or make it into a gift for someone special.

The Research Model

The Research Model gives you a way to approach an issue of significance and explore it. The organization of this model is based on the major elements of the Reasoning Model.

1. **Identify your issue or problem.**
   - What is the issue or problem?
   - Who are the stakeholders and what are their positions?
   - What is my position on this issue?

2. **Read about your issue and identify points of view or arguments through information sources.**
   - What are my print sources?
   - What are my media sources?
   - What are my people sources?
   - What primary and secondary source documents might I use?
   - What are my preliminary findings based on a review of existing sources?

3. **Form a set of questions that can be answered by a specific set of data.**
   - What would be the results of _____?
   - Who would benefit and by how much?
   - Who would be harmed and by how much?
   - My research questions: _____

4. **Gather evidence through research techniques such as surveys, interviews, or analysis of primary and secondary source documents.**
   - What survey questions should I ask?
   - What interview questions should I ask?
   - What generalizations do secondary sources give?
   - What data and evidence can I find in primary sources to support different sides of the issue?

5. **Manipulate and transform data so that they can be interpreted.**

   - How can I summarize what I learned?

   - Should I develop charts, diagrams, or graphs to represent my data?

6. **Draw conclusions and make inferences.**

   - What do the data mean? How can I interpret what I found out?

   - How do the data support my original point of view?

   - How do they support other points of view?

   - What conclusions can I make about the issue?

   - What is my point of view now, based on the data?

7. **Determine implications and consequences.**

   - What are the consequences of following the point of view that I support?

   - Do I know enough or are there now new questions to be answered?

8. **Communicate your findings. (Prepare an oral presentation for classmates based on notes and written report.)**

   - What are my purpose, issue, and point of view, and how will I explain them?

   - What data will I use to support my point of view?

   - How will I conclude my presentation?

The Power of Light

Isaac Bashevis Singer

During World War II, after the Nazis had bombed and bombed the Warsaw ghetto, a boy and a girl were hiding in one of the ruins—David, fourteen years old, and Rebecca, thirteen.

It was winter and bitter cold outside. For weeks Rebecca had not left the dark, partially collapsed cellar that was their hiding place, but every few days David would go out to search for food. All the stores had been destroyed in the bombing, and David sometimes found stale bread, cans of food, or whatever else had been buried. Making his way through the ruins was dangerous. Sometimes bricks and mortar would fall down, and he could easily lose his way. But if he and Rebecca did not want to die from hunger, he had to take the risk.

That day was one of the coldest. Rebecca sat on the ground wrapped in all the garments she possessed; still, she could not get warm. David had left many hours before, and Rebecca listened in the darkness for the sound of his return, knowing that if he did not come back nothing remained to her but death.

Suddenly she heard heavy breathing and the sound of a bundle being dropped. David had made his way home. Rebecca could not help but cry "David!"

"Rebecca!"

In the darkness they embraced and kissed. Then David said, "Rebecca, I found a treasure."

"What kind of treasure?"

"Cheese, potatoes, dried mushrooms, and a package of candy—and I have another surprise for you."

"What surprise?"

"Later."

Both were too hungry for a long talk. Ravenously they ate the frozen potatoes, the mushrooms, and part of the cheese. They each had one piece of candy. Then

From Stories for Children *by Isaac Bashevis Singer. Copyright © 1984 by Isaac Bashevis Singer. Reprinted by permission of Farrar, Straus & Giroux, Inc.*

Rebecca asked, "What is it now, day or night?"

"I think night has fallen," David replied. He had a wristwatch and kept track of day and night and also of the days of the week and the month. After a while Rebecca asked again, "What is the surprise?"

"Rebecca, today is the first day of Hanukkah, and I found a candle and some matches."

"Hanukkah tonight?"

"Yes."

"Oh, my God!"

"I am going to bless the Hanukkah candle," David said.

He lit a match and there was light. Rebecca and David stared at their hiding place—bricks, pipes, and the uneven ground. He lighted the candle. Rebecca blinked her eyes. For the first time in weeks she really saw David. His hair was matted and his face streaked with dirt, but his eyes shone with joy. In spite of the starvation and persecution David had grown taller, and he seemed older than his age and manly. Young as they both were, they had decided to marry if they could manage to escape from war-ridden Warsaw. As a token of their engagement, David had given Rebecca a shiny groschen he found in his pocket on the day when the building where both of them lived was bombed.

Now David pronounced the benediction over the Hanukkah candle, and Rebecca said, "Amen." They had both lost their families, and they had good reason to be angry with God for sending them so many afflictions, but the light of the candle brought peace into their souls. That glimmer of light, surrounded by so many shadows, seemed to say without words: Evil has not yet taken complete dominion. A spark of hope is still left.

For some time David and Rebecca had thought about escaping from Warsaw. But how? The ghetto was watched by the Nazis day and night. Each step was dangerous. Rebecca kept delaying their departure. It would be easier in the summer, she often said, but David knew that in their predicament they had little chance of lasting until then. Somewhere in the forest there were young men and women called partisans who fought the Nazi invaders. David wanted to reach them. Now, by the light of the Hanukkah candle, Rebecca suddenly felt renewed courage. She said, "David, let's leave."

"When?"

"When you think it's the right time," she answered.

"The right time is now," David said. "I have a plan."

For a long time David explained the details of his plan to Rebecca. It was more than risky. The Nazis had enclosed the ghetto with barbed wire and posted guards armed with machine guns on the surrounding roofs. At night searchlights lit up all possible exits from the destroyed ghetto. But in his wanderings through the ruins, David had found an opening to a sewer which he thought might lead to the other side. David told Rebecca that their chances of remaining alive were slim. They could drown in the dirty water or freeze to death. Also, the sewers were full of hungry rats. But Rebecca agreed to take the risk; to remain in the cellar for the winter would mean certain death.

When the Hanukkah light began to sputter and flicker before going out, David and Rebecca gathered their few belongings. She packed the remaining food in a kerchief, and David took his matches and a piece of lead pipe for a weapon.

In moments of great danger people become unusually courageous. David and Rebecca were soon on their way through the ruins. They came to passages so narrow they had to crawl on hands and knees. But the food they had eaten, and the joy the Hanukkah candle had awakened in them, gave them the courage to continue. After some time David found the entrance to the sewer. Luckily the sewage had frozen, and it seemed that the rats had left because of the extreme cold. From time to time David and Rebecca stopped to rest and to listen. After a while they crawled on, slowly and carefully. Suddenly they stopped in their tracks. From above they could hear the clanging of a trolley car. They had reached the other side of the ghetto. All they needed now was to find a way to get out of the sewer and to leave the city as quickly as possible.

Many miracles seemed to happen that Hanukkah night. Because the Nazis were afraid of enemy planes, they had ordered a complete blackout. Because of the bitter cold, there were fewer Gestapo guards. David and Rebecca managed to leave the sewer and steal out of the city without being caught. At dawn they reached a forest where they were able to rest and have a bite to eat.

Even though the partisans were not very far from Warsaw, it took David and Rebecca a week to reach them. They walked at night and hid during the days—sometimes in granaries and sometimes in barns. Some peasants stealthily helped the partisans and those who were running away from the Nazis. From time to time David and Rebecca got a piece of bread, a few potatoes, a radish, or whatever the peasants could spare. In one village they encountered a Jewish partisan who had come to get food for his group. He belonged to the Haganah, an organization that sent men from Israel to rescue Jewish refugees from the Nazis in occupied Poland. This young man brought David and Rebecca to the other partisans who roamed the forest. It was the last day of Hanukkah, and that evening the partisans lit eight candles. Some of them played dreidel on the stump of an oak tree while others kept watch.

From the day David and Rebecca met the partisans, their life became like a tale in a storybook. They joined more and more refugees who all had but one desire—to settle in the Land of Israel. They did not always travel by train or bus. They walked. They slept in stables, in burned-out houses, and wherever they could hide from the enemy. To reach their destination, they had to cross Czechoslovakia, Hungary, and Yugoslavia. Somewhere at the seashore in Yugoslavia, in the middle of the night, a small boat manned by a Haganah crew waited for them, and all the refugees with their meager belongings were packed into it. This all happened silently and in great secrecy, because the Nazis occupied Yugoslavia.

But their dangers were far from over. Even though it was spring, the sea was stormy and the boat was too small for such a long trip. Nazi planes spied the boat and tried without success to sink it with bombs. They also feared the Nazi submarines which were lurking in the depths. There was nothing the refugees could do besides pray to God, and this time God seemed to hear their prayers, because they managed to land safely.

The Jews of Israel greeted them with a love that made them forget their suffering. They were the first refugees who had reached the Holy Land, and they were offered all the help and comfort that could be given. Rebecca and David found relatives in Israel who accepted them with open arms, and although they had become quite emaciated, they were basically healthy and recovered quickly. After some rest they were sent to a special school where foreigners were taught modern Hebrew. Both David and Rebecca were diligent students. After finishing high school, David was able to enter the academy of engineering in Haifa, and Rebecca, who excelled in languages and literature, studied in Tel Aviv—but they always met on weekends. When Rebecca was eighteen, she and David were married. They found a small house with a garden in Ramat Gan, a suburb of Tel Aviv.

I know all this because David and Rebecca told me their story on a Hanukkah evening in their house in Ramat Gan about eight years later. The Hanukkah candles were burning, and Rebecca was frying potato pancakes served with applesauce for all of us. David and I were playing dreidel with their little son, Menahem Eliezer, named after both of his grandfathers. David told me that this large wooden dreidel was the same one the partisans had played with on that Hanukkah evening in the forest of Poland. Rebecca said to me, "If it had not been for that little candle David brought to our hiding place, we wouldn't be sitting here today. That glimmer of light awakened in us a hope and strength we didn't know we possessed. We'll give the dreidel to Menahem Eliezer when he is old enough to understand what we went through and how miraculously we were saved."

Name: _____ Date: _____

 **Activity**
1A

Character Change Map: "The Power of Light"

Directions: Consider the changes in either David or Rebecca from "The Power of Light." Complete the map below to show the changes in the character.

Character: _____

Describe the character at the beginning of the story.
_____

Event #1	The character ...
_____	_____
_____	_____

Event #2	The character ...
_____	_____
_____	_____

Event #3	The character ...
_____	_____
_____	_____

Event #4	The character ...
_____	_____
_____	_____

Describe the character at the end of the story.
_____

Name: _____ Date: _____

Change Model

Directions: List three or more examples for each of the following generalizations about change.

Change is linked to time.

_____

_____

_____

Change is everywhere.

_____

_____

_____

Change may be positive or negative.

_____

_____

_____

Change may be perceived as orderly or random.

_____

_____

_____

Change may happen naturally or may be caused by people.

_____

_____

_____

Change

Literature Web

Directions: Complete the Literature Web for Chapters 1 and 2 of *The Secret Garden.*

Key Words	**Feelings**
_____	_____
_____	_____
_____	_____
_____	_____
_____	_____

Ideas	**Title**	**Images/Symbols**
_____	_____	_____
_____	_____	_____
_____	_____	_____
_____		_____
_____		_____
_____		_____

Structure
_____
_____
_____
_____

Name: _____ Date: _____

Activity
3B

Novel Assignment

Directions: During the course of this unit, you will be required to read two novels and complete several activities related to each one. Please read the requirements and fill in the due dates as instructed by your teacher.

I. The Novels

    A. All students will read *The Secret Garden* by Frances Hodgson Burnett.

    B. Select another novel from the following list:

        1. *Year of Impossible Goodbyes* by Sook Nyul Choi

        2. *Words by Heart* by Ouida Sebestyen

        3. *Taking Sides* by Gary Soto

        4. *Call It Courage* by Armstrong Sperry

        5. *Crispin: The Cross of Lead* by Avi

        6. *Elijah of Buxton* by Christopher Paul Curtis

II. The Activities

Please complete the following activities in your unit notebook as you read the novels. Your teacher will check your unit notebook and evaluate it for completeness, the quality of thinking reflected in entries, links from the reading to your personal experience, and well-chosen support from the books for your responses to questions.

    A. Complete Literature Webs for two chapters of your choice from each novel. See Activities 3C, 3D, 3E, and 3F. **Due Date:** _____ Note that you must complete one of your Literature Webs for *The Secret Garden* before Lesson 12. See Activity 3C. **Due Date:** _____

B. Keep a list of new vocabulary words from the novels in your Vocabulary Journal. Complete Vocabulary Webs for at least two words from each novel. **Due Date:** _____

C. Complete the Change Matrix for Novels for Activity 3G. Include specific evidence from the stories to support the various changes you note on the matrix. You may need to use additional sheets of paper. **Due Date:** _____

D. After completing each novel, complete story maps for *The Secret Garden* and your choice novel. See Activities 3H and 3I. **Due Date:** _____

E. In your Literature Journal, keep a collection of written reflections for each of the books. Make an entry after about every 50 pages, or more frequently if you find something to which you want to respond. Use the following prompts to organize your writing, but you do not need to respond to every prompt in each entry. Your teacher will check your Literature Journal regularly.

   1. What is your reaction to what you read? Describe how you feel and why you think you feel that way.

   2. Write about any experiences you have had that are similar to something that happens in the story, or about a time when you felt the way that one of the characters seems to feel.

   3. Write or note an important or meaningful phrase, sentence, or passage from the reading. Explain why it seems important or meaningful to you.

   4. If something in the story confuses you or brings up questions for you, write about it and try to explain why it confuses you.

   5. Write about evidence in the story that supports the generalizations about change.

F. Participate in a literature circle. You will meet with other students reading your novel several times during the unit to discuss your reading.

Novel Assignment Due Date: _____

Name: _____ Date: _____

 **Activity**
3C

Literature Web

Directions: Complete the Literature Web for one of the chapters from Chapter 3 through 14 of *The Secret Garden*.

Key Words
_____
_____
_____
_____

Feelings
_____
_____
_____
_____

Ideas
_____
_____
_____
_____
_____

Title
_____
_____
_____

Images/Symbols
_____
_____
_____
_____
_____

Structure
_____
_____
_____
_____

Name: _____ Date: _____

Literature Web

Activity
3D

Directions: Complete the Literature Web for one of the chapters from Chapter 15 through the end of *The Secret Garden.*

Key Words	Feelings

Ideas	Title	Images/Symbols

Structure

Name: _____ Date: _____

 **Activity**
3E

Literature Web

Directions: Complete the Literature Web for one of the chapters in your choice novel.

Key Words
_____
_____
_____
_____

Feelings
_____
_____
_____
_____

Ideas
_____
_____
_____
_____
_____
_____

Title
_____
_____
_____
_____

Images/Symbols
_____
_____
_____
_____
_____
_____

Structure
_____
_____
_____
_____

Name: _____ Date: _____

Literature Web

Activity
3F

Directions: Complete the Literature Web for one of the chapters in your choice novel.

Key Words
_____
_____
_____
_____

Feelings
_____
_____
_____
_____

Ideas
_____
_____
_____
_____
_____

Title
_____
_____
_____

Images/Symbols
_____
_____
_____
_____
_____

Structure
_____
_____
_____
_____

Name: _____ Date: _____

Activity 3G

Change Matrix for Novels

Directions: Use this matrix to record your notes about changes you identify in the two novels you are reading for the novel assignment.

Literature	*The Secret Garden*	Choice Novel: _____
Changes in characters: • Changes characters make themselves • Changes in characters caused by their circumstances		
Changes in relationships: • Changes in relationships of characters with one another • Changes in relationships of characters with their environment		
Changes in you as a result of reading: • Changes in your understanding of the world • Changes in your understanding of yourself		

Name: _____ Date: _____

Story Map for
The Secret Garden

Directions: Complete the story map for *The Secret Garden*.

Book Title: _____ Author: _____

Setting
_____
_____

Characters
_____
_____

Plot/Problem
_____
_____

Event 1	**Event 2**	**Event 3**
_____	_____	_____
_____	_____	_____
_____	_____	_____
_____	_____	_____

Outcome/Conclusion
_____
_____

Name: _____ Date: _____

 **Activity**
31

Story Map for Choice Novel

Directions: Complete the story map for your choice novel.

Book Title: _____Author: _____

Setting
_____ _____

Characters
_____ _____

Plot/Problem
_____ _____

Event 1	**Event 2**	**Event 3**
_____ _____ _____ _____	_____ _____ _____ _____	_____ _____ _____ _____

Outcome/Conclusion
_____ _____

Dream Deferred

Langston Hughes

What happens to a dream deferred?

Does it dry up
like a raisin in the sun?
Or fester like a sore—
And then run?
Does it stink like rotten meat?
Or crust and sugar over—
like a syrupy sweet?

Maybe it just sags
like a heavy load.
Or does it explode?

Name: _____   Date: _____

Word Sort

Directions: Cut along the lines below to make 40 small strips, each with one word. Sort the words into piles based on the similarities you see between them. Be prepared to explain why you grouped the words as you did.

SELL	CLOSET	NOR	WORD
ANXIOUS	READ	CHAIR	AND
SAY	ANGRY	PERSON	SAD
BUT	EXCITABLE	YO	SUN
MAKE	AT	LEARN	COLOSSAL
SO	VERY	IN	FROM
SLOWLY	WEARILY	AHA	HE
SHE	IT	TOO	OH
WOW	THEY	CLUMSILY	WE
BY	TO	OR	OUCH

Vocabulary Web

Activity
4B

Directions: Use the Vocabulary Web to organize a word study of *desolate*. Write the sentence from *The Secret Garden* in which the word is used. Then write its definition and its synonyms, antonyms, part of speech, and language of origin. Identify the stem or stems of the word and, if possible, write at least three other words that use one or more of your word's stems. Finally, write a sentence or analogy or draw a picture or diagram using the word or showing its meaning.

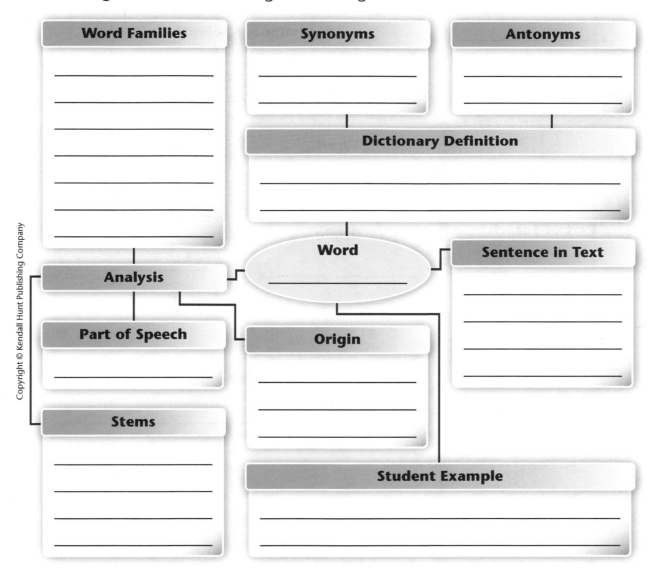

Name: _____ Date: _____

 **Activity
4C**

Vocabulary Web

Directions: Complete the Vocabulary Web for your word.

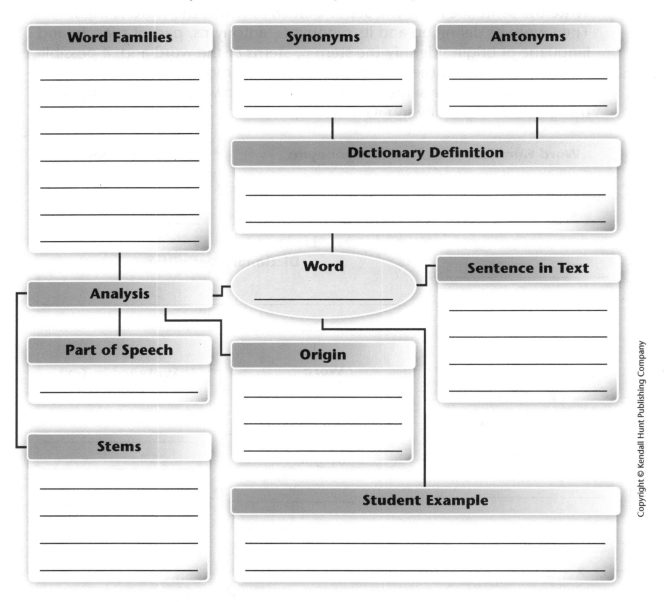

Word Families

_____
_____
_____
_____
_____
_____

Synonyms

_____
_____

Antonyms

_____
_____

Dictionary Definition

_____
_____
_____

Word

_____

Analysis

Part of Speech

_____

Stems

_____
_____
_____

Origin

_____
_____
_____

Sentence in Text

_____
_____
_____
_____

Student Example

_____
_____

Spelling on Social Studies Homework

Activity 5A

Directions: Read and discuss the following paragraph. What reasons are given in the paragraph? Which sentences are most convincing? Which sentences could be improved?

I do not think that teachers should count off for spelling mistakes on social studies homework assignments in the fourth grade. If you have to worry about mechanics, it can distract you from creative ideas. Also, if you don't know how to spell a word, you might not have a dictionary to look it up or a person you can ask. Besides, the point of the assignment is social studies, not English. So that's why I believe teachers should give us a break if we don't spell correctly on our homework in social studies.

Name: _____ Date: _____

Activity 5B

Hamburger Model for Persuasive Writing

Directions: Examine and discuss the Hamburger Model for Persuasive Writing. Look at Activity Page 5A. Identify the parts of the Hamburger Model in that paragraph and write them in this diagram.

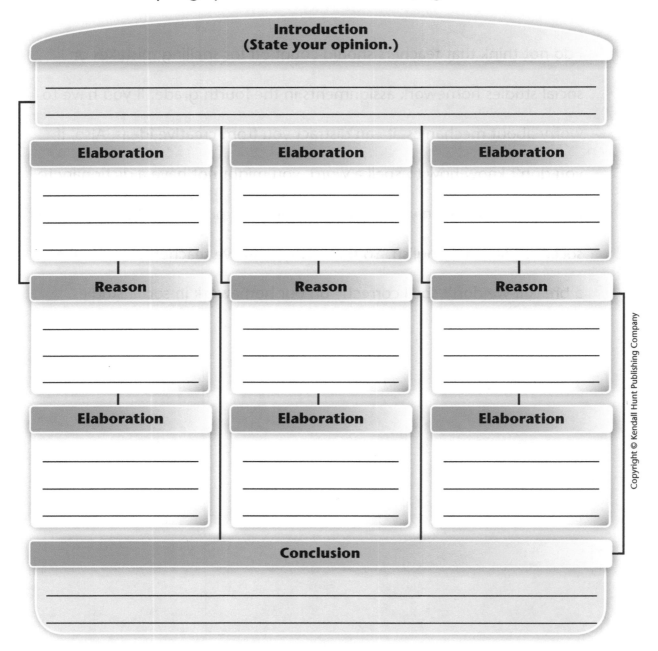

**Introduction
(State your opinion.)**

_____

_____

| **Elaboration** | **Elaboration** | **Elaboration** |

| **Reason** | **Reason** | **Reason** |

| **Elaboration** | **Elaboration** | **Elaboration** |

Conclusion

_____

_____

Jumbled Paragraph

Directions: Cut along the dashed lines below to make strips, each with one sentence. Rearrange the sentences to create a paragraph that makes sense. Use the Hamburger Model as a guide.

Yearly Science Fair Project

Also, if they do a different topic each year, they learn about a new area of study.

This is really important for learning the methods of science.

Yes, I think that students should complete a science fair project every year in grades 4 through 8.

If you only do it once, you won't get the chance to improve.

Lastly, creating a good project takes practice.

First of all, it helps them learn experimental design.

So I think these reasons are enough to convince you that students should do a science fair project each year.

For example, if they do a plant experiment one year they learn some biology, while the next year they could learn some chemistry.

Name: _____ Date: _____

Connect to Mathematics

Directions: Each time your classmates vote on their favorite season, record the results. Then use the grid on the next page to make a double-bar graph to show the results of both votes.

Vote 1			
Spring	**Summer**	**Autumn**	**Winter**

Vote 2			
Spring	**Summer**	**Autumn**	**Winter**

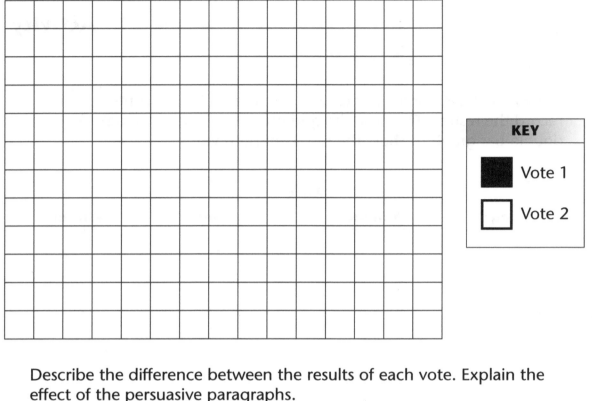

Copyright © Kendall Hunt Publishing Company

Describe the difference between the results of each vote. Explain the effect of the persuasive paragraphs.

_____

_____

_____

_____

_____

_____

_____

_____

_____

_____

Name: _____ Date: _____

Concept Web: Courage in "The Power of Light"

Directions: Examine and discuss the Concept Web about courage in "The Power of Light." Add your own ideas about courage in the story to the web.

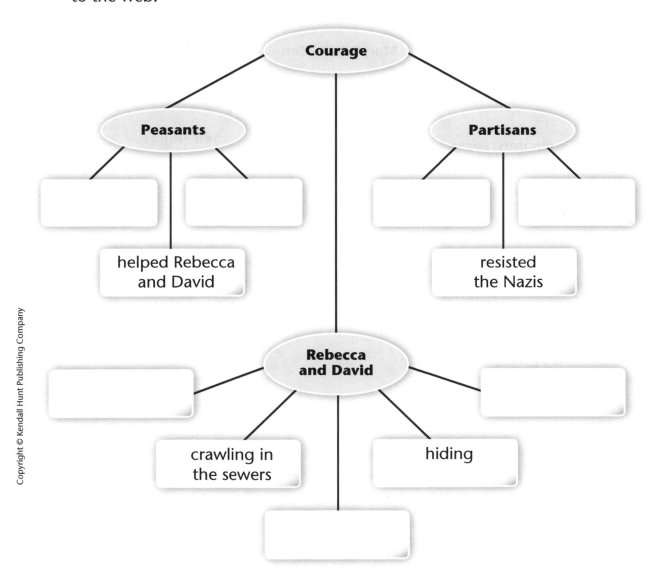

Name: _____ Date: _____

 **Activity 6B**

Concept Web: Mary's Isolation in *The Secret Garden*

Directions: Complete the Concept Web based on *The Secret Garden*.

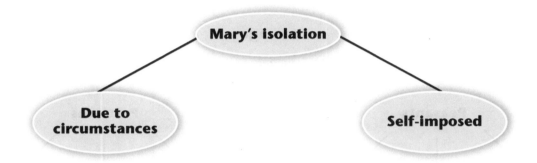

Name: _____ Date: _____

Concept Web: Fear in "The Power of Light"

Directions: Complete the Concept Web about fear in "The Power of Light." Include specific examples from the story. Then write at least two generalizations about fear.

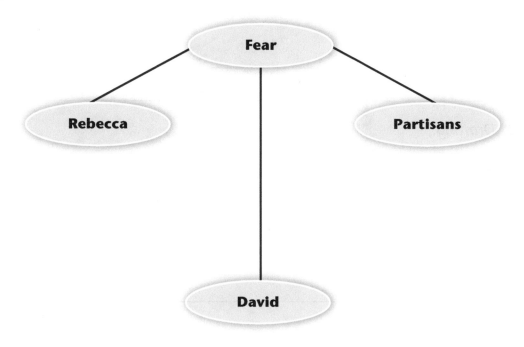

Name: _____ Date: _____

 **Activity**
6D

Writing Process Model

Directions: Use a phrase or sentence to summarize each stage of the writing process. Remember that writers do not always progress through these five stages in order.

1. *Prewriting:*

_____

_____

2. *Drafting:*

_____

_____

3. *Revising:*

_____

_____

4. *Editing:*

_____

_____

5. *Sharing or publishing:*

_____

_____

Name: _____ Date: _____

Self-Review of Writing

Assignment: _____

Directions: Review your writing carefully. For each sentence, circle the choice that best describes your writing. Then complete the two sentences.

1. My main idea is clear.

    Needs improvement   Satisfactory   Excellent

2. My details support the main idea.

    Needs improvement   Satisfactory   Excellent

3. My ideas flow smoothly and in an orderly way.

    Needs improvement   Satisfactory   Excellent

4. The structure clearly follows the Hamburger Model (introduction, body, conclusion).

    Needs improvement   Satisfactory   Excellent

5. My vocabulary is rich and varied.

    Needs improvement   Satisfactory   Excellent

My writing is strong in these ways:

_____

_____

_____

My writing could be improved in these ways:

_____

_____

_____

Name: _____ Date: _____

 **Activity**
6F

Peer Review of Writing

Writer: _____ Assignment: _____

Directions: Read your partner's writing carefully. For each sentence, circle the choice that best describes the writing. Then complete the two sentences.

1. The main idea is clear.
    Needs improvement   Satisfactory   Excellent

2. The details support the main idea.
    Needs improvement   Satisfactory   Excellent

3. The ideas flow smoothly and in an orderly way.
    Needs improvement   Satisfactory   Excellent

4. The structure clearly follows the Hamburger Model (introduction, body, conclusion).
    Needs improvement   Satisfactory   Excellent

5. The vocabulary is rich and varied.
    Needs improvement   Satisfactory   Excellent

The writing is strong in these ways:

_____

_____

_____

The writing could be improved in these ways:

_____

_____

_____

Name: _____ Date: _____

Concept Web: Change in *The Secret Garden*

Directions: Complete the Concept Web based on Chapters 1 and 2 of *The Secret Garden.*

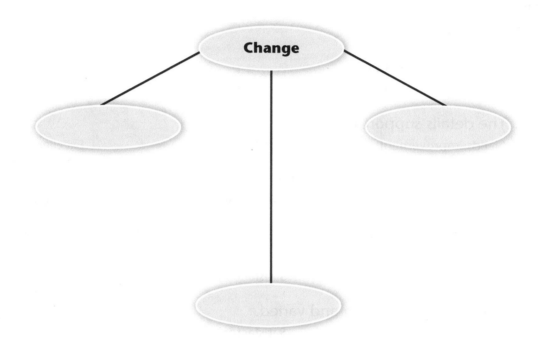

Literary Reflections · Lesson 6 · Concepts and Graphic Organizers

Name: _____ Date: _____

 **Activity**
6H

Review of Writing:
Letter to the Editor

Writer:_____ Publication: _____

Directions: Read the letter to the editor carefully. For each sentence, circle the choice that best describes the writing. Then complete the two sentences.

1. The main idea is clear.
   Needs improvement   Satisfactory   Excellent

2. The details support the main idea.
   Needs improvement   Satisfactory   Excellent

3. The ideas flow smoothly and in an orderly way.
   Needs improvement   Satisfactory   Excellent

4. The structure clearly follows the Hamburger Model (introduction, body, conclusion).
   Needs improvement   Satisfactory   Excellent

5. The vocabulary is rich and varied.
   Needs improvement   Satisfactory   Excellent

The writing is strong in these ways:

_____

_____

_____

The writing could be improved in these ways:

_____

_____

_____

We Live by What We See at Night

Martín Espada

for my father

When the mountains of Puerto Rico
flickered in your sleep
with a moist green light,
when you saw green bamboo hillsides
before waking to East Harlem rooftops
or Texas barracks,
when you crossed the bridge
built by your grandfather
over a river glimpsed
only in interrupted dreaming,
your craving for that island birthplace
burrowed, deep
as thirty years' exile,
constant as your pulse.
This was the inheritance
of your son, born in New York:
that years before
I saw Puerto Rico,
I saw the mountains
looming above the projects,
overwhelming Brooklyn,
living by what I saw at night,
with my eyes closed.

From Being America: Essays on Art, Literature, and Identity from Latin America, *edited by Rachel Weiss.*
Copyright © 1991. Reprinted by permission of Martin Espada.

Border Towns

Roberto Durán

Border towns and brown frowns
and the signs say
get back wet back
souls are searched at night by silver flashlights
gringos and greasers play cat and mouse
and I still wonder why
do apple pies lie?
the signs say live the american way
visit but don't stay
be a friendly neighboor hire good cheap labor
as rows and rows of illegal star war aliens
are aligned and maligned
as the morning shouts fill the morning chill and still
they will not
no way José go away

From Triple Crown *by Roberto Durán. Copyright © 1987 by Bilingual Press/Editorial Bilingüe.*
Reprinted by permission of Bilingual Press/Editorial Bilingüe, Arizona State University, Tempe, AZ.

The Habit of Movement

Judith Ortiz Cofer

Nurtured in the lethargy of the tropics,
the nomadic life did not suit us at first.
We felt like red balloons set adrift
over the wide sky of this new land.
Little by little we lost our will to connect,
and stopped collecting anything heavier
to carry than a wish.
We took what we could from books borrowed
from Greek temples, or holes in the city
walls, returning them hardly handled.

We carried the idea of home on our backs from
house to house, never staying long enough to
learn the secret ways of wood and stone, and
always the blank stare of undraped windows behind
us like the eyes of the unmourned dead.
In time we grew rich in dispossession and
fat with experience.
As we approached but did not touch others,
our habits of movement kept us safe like
a train in motion, nothing could touch us.

From Reaching for the Mainland and Selected New Poems *by Judith Ortiz Cofer. Copyright © 1995 by Bilingual Press/Editorial Bilingue. Reprinted by permission of Bilingual Press/Editorial Bilingue, Arizona State University, Tempe, AZ.*

Name: _____ Date: _____

 **Activity 7A**

Alphabet Book Research Template

Directions: Your teacher will assign you a letter of the alphabet. Investigate an aspect of Hispanic culture that begins with your letter of the alphabet. Use your findings to complete the template. Show the template to your teacher before you create a page based on your findings for a class alphabet book.

Letter of the alphabet: _____

Word or phrase having to do with Hispanic culture: _____

_____

Explain the importance of this word or phrase to Hispanic culture:

_____

_____

_____

_____

_____

_____

_____

_____

_____

_____

_____

_____

_____

Literature Web

Directions: Complete a Literature Web for "We Live by What We See at Night."

Key Words	Feelings
_____	_____
_____	_____
_____	_____
_____	_____
_____	_____

Ideas	Title	Images/Symbols
_____	_____	_____
_____	_____	_____
_____	_____	_____
_____		_____
_____		_____

Structure
_____
_____
_____
_____

Name: _____ Date: _____

Activity
7C

Literature Web

Directions: Complete a Literature Web for your poem.

Key Words
_____
_____
_____
_____
_____

Feelings
_____
_____
_____
_____
_____

Ideas
_____
_____
_____
_____
_____
_____

Title
_____
_____
_____
_____

Images/Symbols
_____
_____
_____
_____
_____
_____

Structure
_____
_____
_____
_____

Art Web

Activity
7D

Directions: Complete the web for *Flying Tiles* by Francisco Toledo or *New York from the Roof Garden* by Rufino Tamayo.

Key Elements

_____
_____
_____
_____
_____
_____

Feelings

_____
_____
_____
_____
_____
_____
_____

Ideas

_____
_____
_____
_____
_____
_____
_____

Title

_____
_____
_____
_____

Images/Symbols

_____
_____
_____
_____
_____
_____
_____

Structure

_____
_____
_____
_____

Name: _____ Date: _____

 **Activity**
7E

Unit Change Matrix

Directions: Use this matrix to record your notes about the changes you read about in the unit literature.

Literature	Internal Changes in Characters	Changes in Relationships with Others or Environment
Hispanic American poems		
African American poems		
"The Old Man and His Affectionate Son"		
"The Weaving of a Dream"		
Emily Dickinson poems		
Your own story		

Another Important Concept of the Reading Selection	Change in Your Understanding of the Other Concept as a Result of Reading

Name: _____ Date: _____

 **Activity 7F**

Vocabulary Web

Directions: Complete the Vocabulary Web for your word.

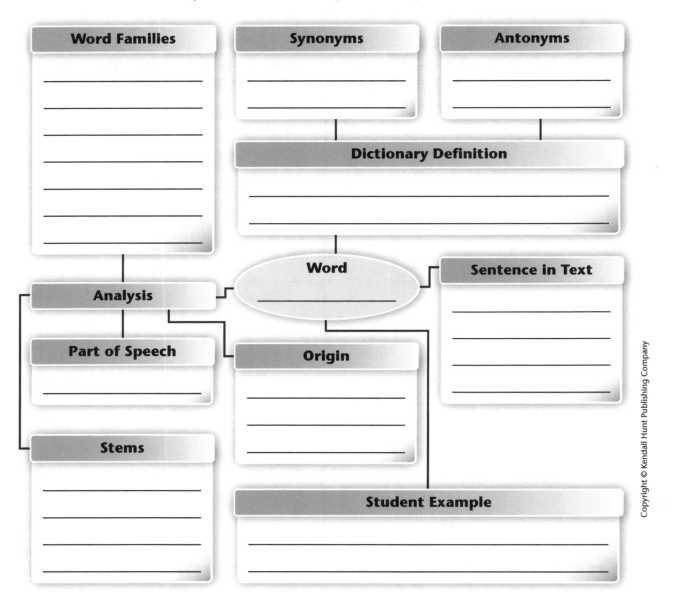

Word Families	Synonyms	Antonyms

Dictionary Definition

Word

Analysis

Part of Speech

Stems

Sentence in Text

Origin

Student Example

Name: _____ Date: _____

Elements of Reasoning

Directions: Read and discuss the Elements of Reasoning.

1. *Purpose or goal:* The purpose or goal is the rationale for reasoning about something. If you are clear about the purpose for your writing and speaking, it will help you focus your message in a coherent direction.

2. *Issue or problem:* The issue or problem is the question to be answered or the issue to be addressed.

3. *Point of view:* The point of view is the perspective of the speaker or author. Other people involved in the issue, called stakeholders, may have different points of view. Stakeholders stand to gain or lose something, depending on how the issue is resolved.

4. *Experiences, data, or evidence:* Experiences, data, and evidence are the details, facts, and information that support the author's or speaker's point of view and help to strengthen an argument.

5. *Concepts or ideas:* Concepts and ideas are the key ideas presented about an issue. Freedom, friendship, and responsibility are examples of concepts.

6. *Assumptions:* Assumptions are the beliefs and understandings that you take for granted about a situation.

7. *Inferences:* An inference is a small step of the mind, in which a person concludes that something is so because of something else being so or seeming to be so.

8. *Implications and consequences:* Implications and consequences are the potential results of following a certain line of reasoning.

Name: _____ Date: _____

 **Activity 8B**

Elements of Reasoning Example

Directions: Take notes responding to each question as your class discusses a problem.

Purpose or goal: What is the purpose of reasoning about this situation?

_____

_____

_____

Issue or problem: What is the problem with which you are dealing?

_____

_____

_____

Point of view: What would each of the people involved think about the problem?

_____

_____

_____

Experiences, data, or evidence: What are the facts that will help you make your decision?

_____

_____

_____

Concepts or ideas: What big ideas are involved in this problem?

_____

_____

_____

Assumptions: What are the assumptions that you or other people involved might make?

_____

_____

_____

Inferences: What are some inferences or small conclusions that you can make based on the facts you have?

_____

_____

_____

Implications and consequences: What might be the consequences of each decision you could make?

_____

_____

_____

Name: _____ Date: _____

Activity 8C

Standards of Reasoning

Directions: Evaluate the argument presented in Activity 5A, "Spelling on Social Studies Homework," by responding to the questions.

Are enough reasons given to make the argument convincing? Explain your answer.

_____

_____

_____

_____

Is the supporting evidence factual and correct? Give an example that supports your response.

_____

_____

_____

_____

Are the reasons clear? Are they explained thoroughly, or is more information needed? Give an example that supports your response.

_____

_____

_____

_____

Are the reasons and evidence specific, or are they general and vague?
Give an example that supports your response.

_____

_____

_____

_____

Are the reasons strong and important, or do they seem to be included just
so that the author has something to say? Give an example that supports
your response.

_____

_____

_____

_____

Is the argument logical? Do the sentences seem to go together, and does
their sequence make sense? Or does the paragraph sound like a set of
disconnected statements? Give an example that supports your response.

_____

_____

_____

_____

Name: _____ Date: _____

 **Activity
8D**

Reasoning About a Situation or Event

Directions: Choose a conflict from one of the unit readings. Use the graphic organizer to analyze the conflict.

Reading: _____

What Is the Situation?
_____

Who are the stakeholders for this situation?	◯	◯	◯	◯
What is the point of view for each stakeholder?	☐	☐	☐	☐
What are the assumptions of each group?	☐	☐	☐	☐
What are the implications of these views?	◯	◯	◯	◯

Name: _____ Date: _____

Standards of Reasoning

Directions: Select an editorial from a newspaper. Evaluate the argument presented in the editorial by responding to the questions.

Are enough reasons given to make the argument convincing? Explain your answer.

_____

_____

_____

_____

Is the supporting evidence factual and correct? Give an example that supports your response.

_____

_____

_____

_____

Are the reasons clear? Are they explained thoroughly, or is more information needed? Give an example that supports your response.

_____

_____

_____

_____

Are the reasons and evidence specific, or are they general and vague?
Give an example that supports your response.

_____

_____

_____

_____

Are the reasons strong and important, or do they seem to be included just
so that the author has something to say? Give an example that supports
your response.

_____

_____

_____

_____

Is the argument logical? Do the sentences seem to go together, and does
their sequence make sense? Or does the paragraph sound like a set of
disconnected statements? Give an example that supports your response.

_____

_____

_____

_____

Name: _____ Date: _____

Reasoning About a Situation or Event

Activity 8F

Directions: Review local newspapers, magazines, and other resources to find information about a conflict in your community or region. Use the graphic organizer to analyze the conflict.

Reading: _____

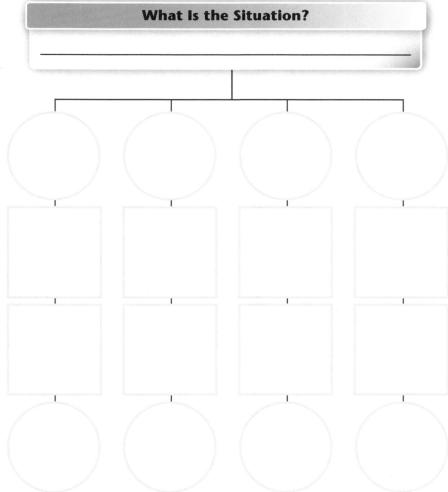

What Is the Situation?

Who are the stakeholders for this situation?

What is the point of view for each stakeholder?

What are the assumptions of each group?

What are the implications of these views?

Monument in Black

Vanessa Howard

Put my Black father on the penny
let him smile at me on the silver dime
put my mother on the dollar
for they've suffered for more than
three eternities of time
and all money can't repay.

Make a monument of my grandfather
let him stand in Washington
for he's suffered more than
three light years
standing idle in the dark
hero of wars that weren't begun.

Name a holiday for my brother
on a sunny day peaceful and warm
for he's fighting for freedom he
won't be granted
all my Black brothers in Vietnam
resting idle in unkept graves.

"Monument in Black" from A Screaming Whisper *by Vanessa Howard. Copyright © 1969 by The Voice of the Children Quarterly. Copyright © 1972 by Vanessa Howard. Reprinted by permission of Henry Holt & Company, LLC.*

Daybreak in Alabama

Langston Hughes

When I get to be a composer
I'm gonna write me some music about
Daybreak in Alabama
And I'm gonna put the purtiest songs in it
Rising out of the ground like a swamp mist
And falling out of heaven like soft dew.
I'm gonna put some tall tall trees in it
And the scent of pine needles
And the smell of red clay after rain
And long red necks
And poppy colored faces
And big brown arms
And the field daisy eyes
Of black and white black white black people
And I'm gonna put white hands
And black hands and brown and yellow hands
And red clay earth hands in it
Touching everybody with kind fingers
And touching each other natural as dew
In that dawn of music when I
Get to be a composer
And write about daybreak
In Alabama.

"Daybreak in Alabama", from The Collected Poems Of Langston Hughes by Langston Hughes, edited by Arnold Rampersad with David Roessel, Associate Editor, copyright © 1994 by The Estate of Langston Hughes. Used by permission of Alfred A. Knopf, a division of Random House, Inc.

Name: _____ Date: _____

Jigsaw Activity

Directions: As you investigate and discuss your topic, list the most important information you and your classmates find about the topic. Identify the information you want to share with your jigsaw group.

Topic

What I Found	What My Classmates Found

What I Want to Share with My Jigsaw Group

Name: _____ Date: _____

 **Activity**
9B

Literature Web

Directions: Complete the Literature Web for your poem.

Key Words
_____
_____
_____
_____
_____

Feelings
_____
_____
_____
_____
_____

Ideas
_____
_____
_____
_____
_____
_____

Title
_____
_____
_____
_____

Images/Symbols
_____
_____
_____
_____
_____
_____

Structure
_____
_____
_____
_____

Name: _____ Date: _____

Vocabulary Web

Directions: Complete the Vocabulary Web for your word.

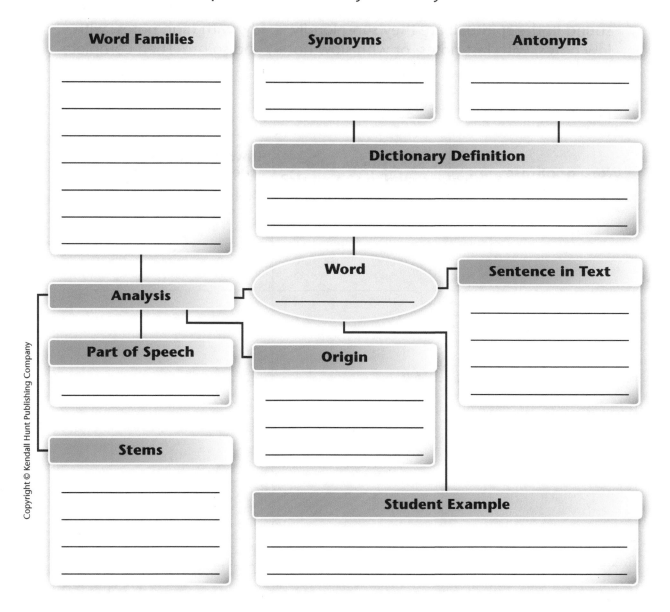

Word Families

_____
_____
_____
_____
_____
_____
_____

Synonyms

_____
_____

Antonyms

_____
_____

Dictionary Definition

_____
_____
_____

Word

_____

Analysis

Sentence in Text

_____
_____
_____

Part of Speech

_____

Origin

_____
_____
_____

Stems

_____
_____
_____
_____

Student Example

_____
_____

Name: _____ Date: _____

 **Activity**
9D

Words in African American Spirituals

Directions: Choose some words or phrases in an African American spiritual and list them in the chart. Listen for how the words or phrases sound in the spiritual: are they sung loudly, softly, with high notes, with low notes, with fast notes, or with slow notes, and so on? Then complete the chart.

Name of Spiritual:_____

Word or phrase	How does the word or phrase sound in the music?	How does the sound affect the meaning of the word or phrase?

Literary Reflections · Lesson 9 · Reflections on African American Poetry

Name: _____ Date: _____

Compare and Contrast Performances of a Spiritual

Directions: Compare and contrast two performances of an African American spiritual by completing the chart.

Name of Spiritual:_____

	Performer #1:	**Performer #2:**
	_____	_____
How are the performances similar?		
How are the performances different?		
How does each performance make you feel?		
Which performance do you prefer? Why?		

Name: _____ Date: _____

Elements of Reasoning: Examining an Issue

Directions: Take notes as you use the Elements of Reasoning to analyze the two viewpoints on an issue discussed in your class.

	Article #1	Article #2
Issue		
Purpose		
Points of View		
Evidence		

	Article #1	Article #2
Concepts		
Assumptions		
Inferences		
Implications and Consequences		

Name: _____ Date: _____

Developing an Issue

Directions: First, state the issue. Next, identify the stakeholder groups and their positions. Finally, state your own initial point of view about the issue.

Developing an Issue
State the issue:

Identify the stakeholder groups:	Describe each group's position:

State your initial position:

Name: _____ Date: _____

 **Activity**
10C

Research Model Planner

Directions: Use this planner to assist you in researching your issue. Respond to each question to the best of your ability, and then make changes to your planner later, as your research progresses. You may record responses on your own paper so that you have enough room for all your ideas.

1. Identify your issue or problem.

   • What is the issue or problem?

   _____

   • Who are the stakeholders and what are their positions?

   _____

   • What is my position on this issue?

   _____

2. Read about your issue and identify points of view or arguments through information sources.

   • What are my print sources?

   _____

   • What are my media sources?

   _____

   • What are my people sources?

   _____

   • What primary and secondary source documents might I use?

   _____

- What are my preliminary findings based on a review of existing sources?

  _____

  _____

3. Form a set of questions that can be answered by a specific set of data.

   - What would be the results of _____?

   - Who would benefit and by how much?

     _____

   - Who would be harmed and by how much?

     _____

   - My research questions:

     _____

     _____

4. Gather evidence through research techniques such as surveys, interviews, or analysis of primary and secondary source documents.

   - What survey questions should I ask?

     _____

     _____

   - What interview questions should I ask?

     _____

     _____

   - What generalizations do secondary sources give?

     _____

• What data and evidence can I find in primary sources to support different sides of the issue?

_____

_____

5. Manipulate and transform data so that they can be interpreted.

• How can I summarize what I learned?

_____

• Should I develop charts, diagrams, or graphs to represent my data?

_____

6. Draw conclusions and make inferences.

• What do the data mean? How can I interpret what I found out?

_____

• How do the data support my original point of view?

_____

• How do they support other points of view?

_____

• What conclusions can I make about the issue?

_____

• What is my point of view now, based on the data?

_____

7. Determine implications and consequences.

- What are the consequences of following the point of view that I support?

  _____

- Do I know enough or are there now new questions to be answered?

  _____

8. Communicate your findings. (Prepare an oral presentation for classmates based on notes and written report.)

- What are my purpose, issue, and point of view, and how will I explain them?

  _____

  _____

- What data will I use to support my point of view?

  _____

- How will I conclude my presentation?

  _____

  _____

Name: _____ Date: _____

 **Activity 10D**

Developing an Issue: Unit Research Project

Directions: First, state the issue. Next, identify the stakeholder groups and their positions. Finally, state your own initial point of view about the issue.

Developing an Issue	
State the issue: _____ _____ _____ _____ _____ _____	
Identify the stakeholder groups: _____ _____ _____ _____ _____	**Describe each group's position:** _____ _____ _____ _____ _____
State your initial position: _____ _____ _____ _____ _____	

Name: _____ Date: _____

Research Tracking Form

Directions: Note the date that you complete each activity in order to track your progress on the unit research project.

_____ 1. **Identify your issue or problem.**
What is the issue or problem?
Who are the stakeholders and what are their positions?
What is my position on this issue?

_____ 2. **Read about your issue and identify points of view or arguments through information sources.**
What are my print sources?
What are my media sources?
What are my people sources?
What primary and secondary source documents might I use?
What are my preliminary findings based on a review of existing sources?

_____ 3. **Form a set of questions that can be answered by a specific set of data.**
What would be the results of _____?
Who would benefit and by how much?
Who would be harmed and by how much?
My research questions: _____

_____ 4. **Gather evidence through research techniques such as surveys, interviews, or analysis of primary and secondary source documents.**
What survey questions should I ask?
What interview questions should I ask?
What generalizations do secondary sources give?
What data and evidence can I find in primary sources to support different sides of the issue?

_____ 5. **Manipulate and transform data so that they can be interpreted.**
How can I summarize what I learned?
Should I develop charts, diagrams, or graphs to represent my data?

_____ 6. **Draw conclusions and make inferences.**
What do the data mean? How can I interpret what I found out?
How do the data support my original point of view?
How do they support other points of view?
What conclusions can I make about the issue?
What is my point of view now, based on the data?

_____ 7. **Determine implications and consequences.**
What are the consequences of following the point of view that I support?
Do I know enough or are there now new questions to be answered?

_____ 8. **Communicate your findings. (Prepare an oral presentation for classmates based on notes and written report.)**
What are my purpose, issue, and point of view, and how will I explain them?
What data will I use to support my point of view?
How will I conclude my presentation?

Name: _____ Date: _____

Characteristics of an Issue

Directions: Respond to the following questions to help you define a possible issue for research.

1. Why is this issue an example of a real-world problem?

_____

_____

_____

_____

_____

2. Who are the stakeholders? What might they win or lose?

_____

_____

_____

_____

_____

3. What are the different points of view of each of the stakeholders about the issue?

_____

_____

_____

_____

_____

4. What evidence supports the different points of view about the issue?

_____

_____

_____

_____

_____

5. Why does the issue matter to you? Why would you want to spend time researching it?

_____

_____

_____

_____

_____

Name: _____ Date: _____

Propaganda Techniques

What Is Propaganda?

Propaganda is the spreading of information—including facts, ideas, rumors, half-truths, and even lies—to influence the public.

What Techniques Are Used in Propaganda?

The following propaganda techniques are used in persuasive messages, including advertisements.

Appeals to superstition, for example: *During the downtown renewal project, you won't have to walk under any ladders to get to the bargains in our store.*

Appeals to ignorance, for example: *Have you gone to other doctors and found no cure? Now come to me, Doctor X. I can cure heart trouble, cancer, headaches, and nervous conditions through the adjustment of the spine, which controls all body functions.*

Ego trips, for example: *It costs a little more, but aren't you worth it?*

Circular logic, for example: *Our computer dating service has matched up hundreds of happy couples, many of whom are now happily married, so what are you waiting for? Join now!*

Appeals to emotion, for example: *Prowlers are on the loose in our town—keep your family safe! Call ABC Burglar Alarms today.*

Faulty use of statistics, for example: *Mary B. lost 30 pounds in 24 days! Our weight loss graduates lose more weight than participants in any other program.*

Vagueness, for example: *Everyone is talking about the new Corvette!*

Word choice, including such words as *super, great, best ever, astonishing,* and *new.*

Repetition, especially of slogans, such as: *Eat better, feel better, live better!*

Exaggeration, which is related to word choice; for example: *Come in today! Don't miss the sale of a lifetime!*

Quoting out of context, for example: an ad for a book says, *Pattonville Times says, "Bigger-than-life characters have appeal ...."* The actual review in the *Pattonville Times* said, "Not worth reading. Bigger-than-life characters have appeal only when handled by a competent author, and this author is certainly not competent."

Omitting important facts, for example: *She was treated in a mental hospital.* The "she" in question was injured in an automobile accident and taken to the nearest emergency room, which happened to be in a hospital most noted for its treatment of mental patients.

The get-on-the-bandwagon approach, for example: *Don't miss this big event. EVERYONE will be there!*

"He's just one of the boys", for example: *Vote for Mr. X. Born and raised in this town, he knows us folks and our problems.*

Snob appeal, for example: *For those who want the very best!* or: *Where the great meet to eat.*

Name dropping, for example by proclaiming that the movie star Ms. X uses this brand.

Testimonials, for example: *Hospital tested! Recommended by more doctors than any other brand.*

Name: _____ Date: _____

Propaganda Techniques in Advertisements

Activity 11B

Directions: Complete the chart. Identify the propaganda techniques used in your advertisements. Then describe how the advertisement uses the technique.

Propaganda Technique	Advertisement	How the Advertisement Uses the Technique
Appeal to superstition		
Appeal to ignorance		
Ego trip		
Circular logic		
Appeal to emotion		
Faulty use of statistics		
Vagueness		

Propaganda Technique	Advertisement	How the Advertisement Uses the Technique
Word choice		
Repetition (including use of a slogan)		
Exaggeration		
Quoting out of context		
Omitting important facts		
The get-on-the-bandwagon approach		
"He's just one of the boys"		
Snob appeal		
Name dropping		
Testimonials		

Literary Reflections · Lesson 11 · Persuasive Messages

Name: _____ Date: _____

Propaganda Techniques in Your Classmates' Advertisements

Activity 11C

Directions: Complete the chart. Identify the propaganda techniques used in your classmates' advertisements. Describe their effects.

Advertisement	Propaganda Techniques	Effects of the Techniques

Name: _____ Date: _____

 **Activity 11D**

Propaganda Techniques in Commercials for Children

Directions: Complete the chart. List television commercials that are directed at children. Identify the product being advertised, the propaganda techniques used, and any evidence given to persuade the viewer.

Product Advertised	Propaganda Techniques	Evidence Used to Persuade

Name: _____ Date: _____

Propaganda Techniques in Election Campaigns

Activity 11E

Directions: Complete the chart. List candidates and their messages. Identify the propaganda techniques used and any evidence given to persuade the reader.

Candidate and Message	Propaganda Techniques	Evidence Used to Persuade

I never saw a moor,
I never saw the sea;
Yet know I how the heather looks,
And what a wave must be.

I never spoke with God,
Nor visited in heaven;
Yet certain am I of the spot
As if the chart were given.

—Emily Dickinson

Name: _____ Date: _____

Activity
12A *The Secret Garden* **Project List**

Directions: Select and complete one of the following projects about *The Secret Garden.*

- Write a poem about the "wuthering" wind.

- Draw or paint a picture of the moor or the secret garden as it looks when Mary first enters it.

- Write a letter that Mrs. Craven might have written to her son before she died about the secret garden.

- Create a map of the gardens of Misselthwaite Manor, based on information in *The Secret Garden,* an investigation of traditional English gardens, and your imagination.

- Make a gardening catalogue of the plants described in the book. Find out what the plants look like and the kind of care they need, and illustrate and describe them in the catalogue.

- Locate the Yorkshire moors on a map of England. Find information about the plants and animals of the moor and the climate of that area of the world. Write an essay comparing the information you found with the descriptions of the moor in the novel.

- Make a dictionary of the Yorkshire words and phrases used in the book. Identify the words that describe things specific to that part of the world, such as "wuthering."

- Study the relationship between India and the British Empire. Prepare a report to present to your classmates.

- Select five of your favorite quotations from the book. Illustrate each one to display in the classroom.

- Find out more about the life and career of the author, Frances Hodgson Burnett. Prepare a PowerPoint presentation to share with your classmates.

- Select a chapter that features multiple characters and dialogue. Create a Readers' Theatre script based on the chapter, rehearse it with several of your classmates, and present it to the rest of the class.

Name: _____ Date: _____

The Secret Garden
Writing Assignment

Activity 12B

Directions: Select one of the following statements about *The Secret Garden.* Use the Hamburger Model to write a paragraph or essay defending or opposing the statement. Use specific examples from the novel to support your ideas. Use the space on this page to brainstorm and organize ideas for the essay.

- The secret garden is a symbol for Mary and Colin.
- Mary's discussions with Martha show evidence of the ways she is changing.
- Dickon and the robin are symbols of friendship and spring.
- When people stop feeling sorry for themselves and start thinking of others, it helps them to grow.
- The changes in the seasons parallel the changes in Mary and Colin's lives.

Name: _____ Date: _____

Activity
12C

Compare and Contrast
Mary and Sara

Directions: Write similarities between Mary Lennox in *The Secret Garden* and Sara Crewe in *A Little Princess* in the "Both" section of the diagram. Then tell how the two characters are different. Write descriptions that only tell about Mary in the "Mary" section. Write descriptions that only tell about Sara in the "Sara" section.

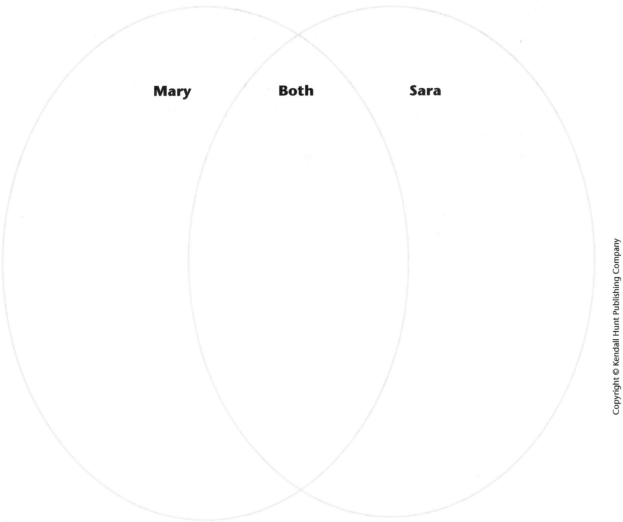

Mary   **Both**   **Sara**

The Old Man and His Affectionate Son

A Japanese folktale

Once upon a time, there lived a son who was very dutiful and devoted to his father. In those days, it is said, there was a law requiring aged parents, who could no longer work, to be carried to and discarded in the mountains.

The affectionate son's father also grew old and was no longer able to work. Now that the time came to discard him, the son one day set out with the father on his back and went deep into the mountains. While being carried on the son's back, the father who loved him dearly, tore off twigs of trees and dropped them to the ground as guiding marks for fear the son might get lost on his way back.

Far up in a mountain, the son spread leaves at a spot which was sheltered from the rain and placed the father on the leaves. "Now, my dear father," he said, "I must bid you farewell." Thereupon, the father broke off a nearby twig, and showing it to the son, said: "Dear son, lest you should lose your way, I have dropped twigs like this on the ground so that you may find your way. The twigs will guide you home. Now, good-bye, dear son!" Moved to tears by his father's affection, the son could not leave him behind and carried him back down the mountain.

However, if this became known to the lord of the country, both the parent and the son would be severely punished. So the son dug a cave in the back yard and hid his father there. Every day, he carried meals to his father in the cave, and whenever he obtained a delicacy, he never failed to share it with him.

One day, the lord put up notices in various parts of the country, calling upon people to submit "ropes made of ashes." Everybody was at a loss how to twist ashes into ropes, and in the village where the dutiful son lived, no one could

From: Folk Tales of Old Japan (1975). *Tokyo: The Japan Times, Ltd.*

solve this difficult problem, either.

Upon learning of this, the father said to his son: "Strand a rope tightly and burn it on a board." When the son did just as the father had told him to, a rope of ashes was formed. He took it to the lord and received high praise for having solved the difficult problem.

Shortly after that, the lord showed him a simple wooden pole which retained no traces of its original shape, and ordered him to confirm which end of the pole had been the root. The son brought the pole back home and asked his father what to do. The father said to him: "Put the pole slowly into the water. The end which floats lightly is the head, and the end which tends to dip into the water is the root."

The son tested the pole according to his father's instruction and reported the result to the lord. Impressed with the fine settlement of the second difficult problem as well, the lord warmly praised the son.

However, the lord then came up with a third knotty problem, which was more difficult than the previous two. That is, he ordered the son to make a "drum that can be sounded even without beating."

The son again consulted his father, who immediately said: "Well, nothing could be easier, son. Go and buy leather. Then go to the mountain and bring a beehive." The son did as instructed and the father made him a drum with the beehive in it. "Take this to the lord," he said to the son.

Promptly, the son took the drum to the lord. When the lord touched the drum, the surprised bees within flew about and bumped into the leather membranes. Consequently, the drum started to sound.

Complimenting the son on the remarkable solution of the three difficult problems in succession, the lord asked him how he could manage to find such wonderful solutions.

The son replied: "Being too young to have enough experience and wisdom, I could not work out any of the problems. To tell the truth, I obtained all the solutions from my old father, rich in experience and wisdom." Tearfully, he confided everything, saying:

"I could not leave my father behind in the mountain, so I have hidden him in my home."

Impressed with the son's story, the lord said, "Well, I did not know old people were so sagacious and valuable. From now on, nobody will be allowed to cast off old parents in the mountains." After that, it is said, old people spent happy lives with their young.

Name: _____ Date: _____

Developing an Issue

Directions: First, state the issue. Next, identify the stakeholder groups and their points of view. Finally, state your own initial point of view about the issue.

Developing an Issue
State the issue: _____   _____   _____   _____

Identify the stakeholder groups:	Describe each group's point of view:
_____ _____ _____ _____ _____ _____ _____	_____ _____ _____ _____ _____ _____ _____

State your initial point of view: _____   _____   _____   _____

Name: _____ Date: _____

 **Activity 13B**

Literature Web

Directions: Complete the Literature Web for "The Old Man and His Affectionate Son."

Key Words
_____
_____
_____
_____

Feelings
_____
_____
_____
_____

Ideas
_____
_____
_____
_____
_____

Title
_____
_____
_____

Images/Symbols
_____
_____
_____
_____
_____

Structure
_____
_____
_____

Name: _____ Date: _____

Characteristics of a Folktale

Directions: Though not every folktale has exactly the same characteristics, folktales generally share some common characteristics. List examples from "The Old Man and His Affectionate Son" that illustrate the following characteristics of a folktale.

- A folktale uses such phrases as "once upon a time" or "long, long ago."

_____

_____

_____

_____

- A folktale uses the number three: three characters, three events, three tasks, etc.

_____

_____

_____

_____

_____

- The characters are common people and animals.

_____

_____

_____

_____

_____

• The story includes good and bad characters.

_____

_____

_____

_____

• The good characters have a problem to solve.

_____

_____

_____

_____

• Phrases or responses are repeated.

_____

_____

_____

_____

• The story has a happy ending.

_____

_____

_____

_____

Name: _____ Date: _____

Jigsaw Activity

Directions: As you investigate and discuss your topic, list the most important information you and your classmates find about the topic. Identify the information you want to share with your jigsaw group.

Topic

What I Found	What My Classmates Found

What I Want to Share with My Jigsaw Group

Name: _____ Date: _____

 **Activity**
13E

Self-Review of Writing

Assignment:_____

Directions: Review your writing carefully. For each sentence, circle the choice that best describes your writing. Then complete the two sentences.

1. My main idea is clear.
   Needs improvement   Satisfactory   Excellent

2. My details support the main idea.
   Needs improvement   Satisfactory   Excellent

3. My ideas flow smoothly and in an orderly way.
   Needs improvement   Satisfactory   Excellent

4. The structure clearly follows the Hamburger Model (introduction, body, conclusion).
   Needs improvement   Satisfactory   Excellent

5. My vocabulary is rich and varied.
   Needs improvement   Satisfactory   Excellent

My writing is strong in these ways:

_____

_____

_____

My writing could be improved in these ways:

_____

_____

_____

Name: _____ Date: _____

Peer Review of Writing

Writer:_____ Assignment: _____

Directions: Read your partner's writing carefully. For each sentence, circle the choice that best describes the writing. Then complete the two sentences.

1. The main idea is clear.
   Needs improvement   Satisfactory   Excellent

2. The details support the main idea.
   Needs improvement   Satisfactory   Excellent

3. The ideas flow smoothly and in an orderly way.
   Needs improvement   Satisfactory   Excellent

4. The structure clearly follows the Hamburger Model (introduction, body, conclusion).
   Needs improvement   Satisfactory   Excellent

5. The vocabulary is rich and varied.
   Needs improvement   Satisfactory   Excellent

The writing is strong in these ways:

_____

_____

_____

The writing could be improved in these ways:

_____

_____

_____

Name: _____ Date: _____

 **Activity**
13G

Vocabulary Web

Directions: Complete a Vocabulary Web for your word.

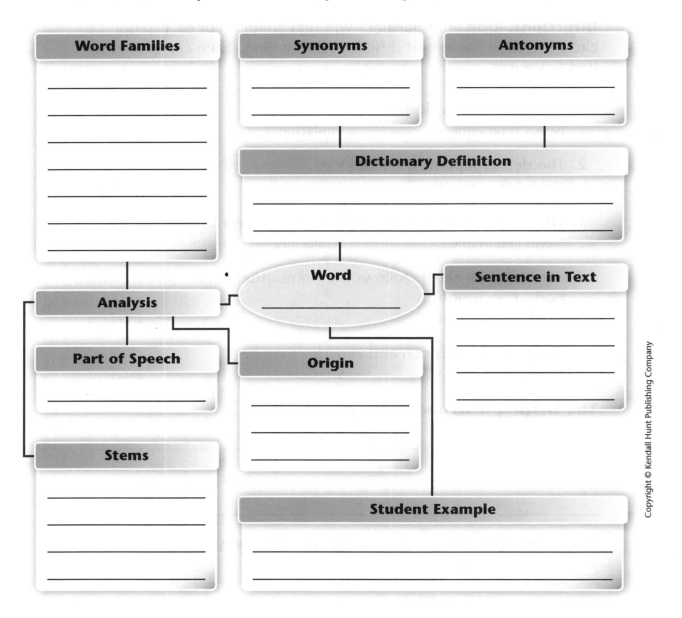

Word Families
_____
_____
_____
_____
_____
_____

Synonyms
_____
_____

Antonyms
_____
_____

Dictionary Definition
_____
_____

Word
_____

Analysis

Part of Speech
_____

Stems
_____
_____

Origin
_____
_____
_____

Sentence in Text
_____
_____
_____

Student Example
_____
_____

Name: _____ Date: _____

Developing an Issue

Directions: First, state the issue. Next, identify the stakeholder groups and their points of view. Finally, state your own initial point of view about the issue.

Developing an Issue
State the issue: _____   _____   _____   _____

Identify the stakeholder groups:	Describe each group's point of view:
_____ _____ _____ _____ _____ _____ _____ _____	_____ _____ _____ _____ _____ _____ _____

| State your initial point of view:

 _____
 _____
 _____
 _____ |

Name: _____ Date: _____

Persuasion Chart

Directions: List examples of people you have tried to persuade at some point, what you tried to persuade them to do, how you tried to persuade them, and what the results were. Record your responses on the chart.

Who: Who was the audience?	**What:** What was the issue you were addressing?	**How:** What arguments did you use?	**Results:** How successful were you in persuading your audience?		

Who:	What:	How:	Results:
Who was the audience?	What was the issue you were addressing?	What arguments did you use?	How successful were you in persuading your audience?

Name: _____ Date: _____

Oral Presentation
Evaluation Form

Speaker: _____ Assignment: _____

Directions: For items 1–10, circle the choice that best describes the presentation. Then complete the two sentences.

Content

1. The purpose of the presentation was clear.
   Needs improvement   Satisfactory   Excellent

2. The speaker included details that supported the main idea.
   Needs improvement   Satisfactory   Excellent

3. The speaker showed knowledge of the subject.
   Needs improvement   Satisfactory   Excellent

4. The speaker used vocabulary that was rich and varied.
   Needs improvement   Satisfactory   Excellent

Organization

5. The speech followed the Hamburger Model, with a clear introduction, body, and conclusion.
   Needs improvement   Satisfactory   Excellent

6. The ideas flowed smoothly and in an orderly way.
   Needs improvement   Satisfactory   Excellent

7. The speaker closed the presentation with a strong, interesting idea that restated the purpose.
   Needs improvement   Satisfactory   Excellent

Delivery

8. The speaker made good eye contact with the audience.

    Needs improvement   Satisfactory   Excellent

9. The speaker spoke loudly enough for the entire audience to hear.

    Needs improvement   Satisfactory   Excellent

10. The speaker's words were clear and could be understood.

    Needs improvement   Satisfactory   Excellent

The best part of this presentation was:

_____

_____

_____

_____

_____

_____

_____

A suggestion for improvement is:

_____

_____

_____

_____

_____

_____

_____

_____

Name: _____ Date: _____

Preparing for an
Oral Presentation

Activity
14C

Directions: Use the organizer to prepare notes for an oral presentation.

INTRODUCTION:
What is the issue? What is your point of view?

REASONS:
What reasons support your point of view?

CONCLUSION:
With what idea or ideas do you want to leave your audience?

Name: _____ Date: _____

 **Activity 14D**

Oral Presentation Evaluation Form

Speaker: _____ Assignment: _____

Directions: For items 1–10, circle the choice that best describes the speech. Then complete the two sentences.

Content

1. The purpose of the speech was clear.
   Needs improvement   Satisfactory   Excellent

2. The speaker included details that supported the main idea.
   Needs improvement   Satisfactory   Excellent

3. The speaker showed knowledge of the subject.
   Needs improvement   Satisfactory   Excellent

4. The speaker used vocabulary that was rich and varied.
   Needs improvement   Satisfactory   Excellent

Organization

5. The speech followed the Hamburger Model, with a clear introduction, body, and conclusion.
   Needs improvement   Satisfactory   Excellent

6. The ideas flowed smoothly and in an orderly way.
   Needs improvement   Satisfactory   Excellent

7. The speaker closed the presentation with a strong, interesting idea that restated the purpose.
   Needs improvement   Satisfactory   Excellent

Delivery

8. The speaker made good eye contact with the audience.

Needs improvement Satisfactory Excellent

9. The speaker spoke loudly enough for the entire audience to hear.

Needs improvement Satisfactory Excellent

10. The speaker's words were clear and could be understood.

Needs improvement Satisfactory Excellent

The best part of this speech was:

_____

_____

_____

_____

_____

_____

_____

A suggestion for improvement is:

_____

_____

_____

_____

_____

_____

_____

Name: _____ Date: _____

Literature Web

Directions: Complete the Literature Web for *The Weaving of a Dream.*

Key Words

_____
_____
_____
_____
_____

Feelings

_____
_____
_____
_____
_____
_____

Ideas

_____
_____
_____
_____
_____
_____

Title

_____
_____
_____
_____

Images/Symbols

_____
_____
_____
_____
_____
_____

Structure

_____
_____
_____
_____

Name: _____ Date: _____

 **Activity**
15B

Compare and Contrast
Two Folktales

Directions: Complete the Venn diagram about the Japanese and Chinese folktales.

Japanese Folktale   **Both**   **Chinese Folktale**

Characteristics of a Folktale

Activity 15C

Directions: List examples from *The Weaving of a Dream* that illustrate the following characteristics of a folktale.

- A folktale uses such phrases as "once upon a time" or "long, long ago."

_____

_____

_____

_____

_____

- A folktale uses the number three: three characters, three events, three tasks, etc.

_____

_____

_____

_____

_____

- The characters are common people and animals.

_____

_____

_____

_____

_____

- The story includes good and bad characters.

_____

_____

_____

_____

_____

- The good characters have a problem to solve.

_____

_____

_____

_____

- Phrases or responses are repeated.

_____

_____

_____

_____

- The story has a happy ending.

_____

_____

_____

_____

Name: _____ Date: _____

Vocabulary Web

Directions: Complete a Vocabulary Web for your word.

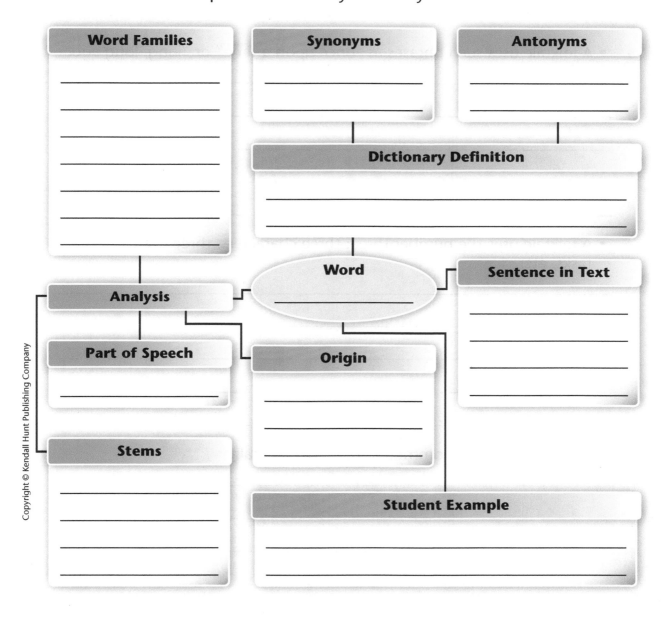

Word Families
_____
_____
_____
_____
_____
_____

Synonyms
_____
_____

Antonyms
_____
_____

Dictionary Definition
_____
_____

Word
_____

Analysis

Sentence in Text
_____
_____
_____
_____

Part of Speech
_____

Origin
_____
_____
_____

Stems
_____
_____
_____

Student Example
_____
_____

Name: _____ Date: _____

 **Activity**
15E **Characteristics of a Folktale**

Directions: List the examples from your story that illustrate the following characteristics of a folktale.

• A folktale uses such phrases as "once upon a time" or "long, long ago."

_____

_____

_____

_____

_____

• A folktale uses the number three: three characters, three events, three tasks, etc.

_____

_____

_____

_____

_____

• The characters are common people and animals.

_____

_____

_____

_____

_____

• The story includes good and bad characters.

_____

_____

_____

_____

• The good characters have a problem to solve.

_____

_____

_____

_____

• Phrases or responses are repeated.

_____

_____

_____

_____

• The story has a happy ending.

_____

_____

_____

_____

Name: _____ Date: _____

 **Activity**
15F

Compare and Contrast Two Folktales

Directions: Complete the Venn diagram about *The Weaving of a Dream* and the myth of Pandora's box.

The Weaving of a Dream

Both

Pandora's box

Literary Reflections · Lesson 15 · A Chinese Folktale

Presentiment is that long shadow on the lawn
Indicative that suns go down;
The notice to the startled grass
That darkness is about to pass.

—Emily Dickinson

Funny to be a century,
And see the people going by—
I should die of the oddity,
But then, I'm not so staid as he.

He keeps his secrets safely—very;
Were he to tell, extremely sorry
This bashful globe of ours would be—
So dainty of publicity.

—Emily Dickinson

The morns are meeker than they were,
The nuts are getting brown,
The berry's cheek is plumper,
The rose is out of town.

The maple wears a gayer scarf,
The field a scarlet gown.
Lest I should be old-fashioned,
I'll put a trinket on.

—Emily Dickinson

It sifts from leaden sieves,
It powders all the wood,
It fills with alabaster wool
The wrinkles of the road.

It makes an even face
Of mountain and of plain—
Unbroken forehead from the east
Unto the east again.

It reaches to the fence,
It wraps it, rail by rail,
Till it is lost in fleeces.
It flings a crystal veil

On stump and stack and stem—
The summer's empty room,
Acres of seams where harvests were,
Recordless, but for them.

It ruffles wrists of posts,
As ankles of a queen—
Then stills its artisans like ghosts,
Denying they have been.

—Emily Dickinson

Dear March, come in!
How glad I am!
I looked for you before.
Put down your hat—
You must have walked—
How out of breath you are!
Dear March, how are you?
And the rest?
Did you leave Nature well?
Oh, March, come right upstairs with me,
I have so much to tell!

I got your letter, and the birds'—
The maples never knew
That you were coming—I declare,
How red their faces grew!
But, March, forgive me—
And all those hills
You left for me to hue—
There was no purple suitable,
You took it all with you.

Who knocks? That April!
Lock the door!
I will not be pursued!
He stayed away a year, to call
When I am occupied.
But trifles look so trivial
As soon as you have come,
That blame is just as dear as praise
And praise as mere as blame.

—Emily Dickinson

Name: _____ Date: _____

 **Activity 16A**

Literature Web

Directions: Complete the Literature Web for the poem assigned to you.

Key Words	Feelings
_____	_____
_____	_____
_____	_____
_____	_____
_____	_____
	_____

Ideas	Title	Images/Symbols
_____	_____	_____
_____	_____	_____
_____	_____	_____
_____	_____	_____
_____		_____
_____		_____
		_____

Structure
_____
_____
_____
_____

Name: _____ Date: _____

Hamburger Model

Directions: Use the Hamburger Model to plan a paragraph explaining why the title you wrote for a poem by Emily Dickinson is a good one.

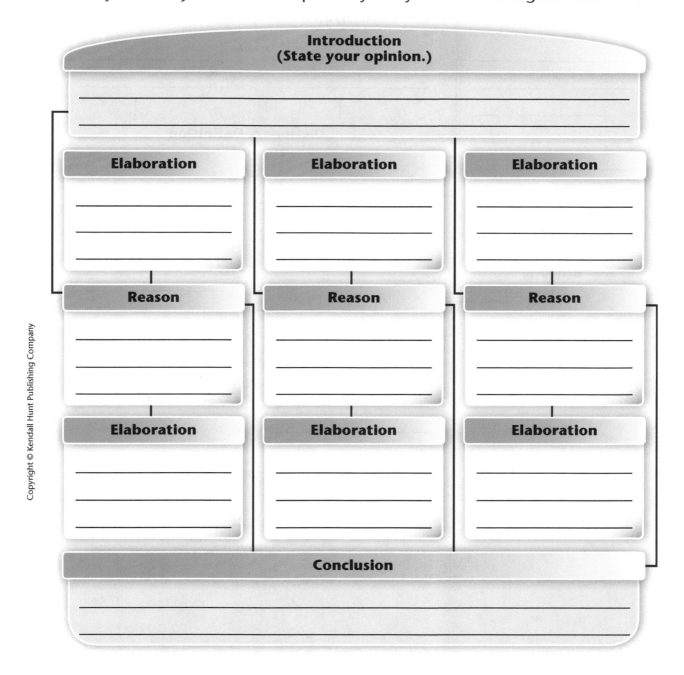

Introduction
(State your opinion.)

_____
_____

Elaboration

_____
_____
_____

Elaboration

_____
_____
_____

Elaboration

_____
_____
_____

Reason

_____
_____
_____

Reason

_____
_____
_____

Reason

_____
_____
_____

Elaboration

_____
_____
_____

Elaboration

_____
_____
_____

Elaboration

_____
_____
_____

Conclusion

_____
_____

Name: _____ Date: _____

 **Activity 16C**

Vocabulary Web

Directions: Complete a Vocabulary Web for your word.

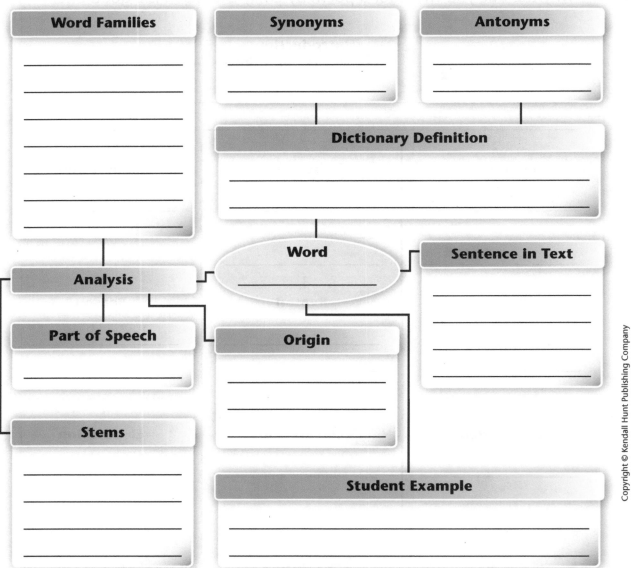

Literary Reflections· Lesson 16 · Reflections on Change in Poetry

I'm Nobody! Who are you?
Are you—Nobody—too?
Then there's a pair of us!
Don't tell! they'd banish us—you know!

How dreary—to be—Somebody!
How public—like a Frog—
To tell your name—the livelong June—
To an admiring Bog!

—Emily Dickinson

Name: _____ Date: _____

Activity
17A

Oral Presentation Evaluation Form

Directions: For items 1–10, circle the choice that best describes the presentation. Then complete the two sentences.

Content

1. The purpose of the presentation was clear.
   Needs improvement   Satisfactory   Excellent

2. The speaker included details that supported the main idea.
   Needs improvement   Satisfactory   Excellent

3. The speaker showed knowledge of the subject.
   Needs improvement   Satisfactory   Excellent

4. The speaker used vocabulary that was rich and varied.
   Needs improvement   Satisfactory   Excellent

Organization

5. The speech followed the Hamburger Model, with a clear introduction, body, and conclusion.
   Needs improvement   Satisfactory   Excellent

6. The ideas flowed smoothly and in an orderly way.
   Needs improvement   Satisfactory   Excellent

7. The speaker closed the presentation with a strong, interesting idea that restated the purpose.
   Needs improvement   Satisfactory   Excellent

Delivery

8. The speaker made good eye contact with the audience.

    Needs improvement   Satisfactory   Excellent

9. The speaker spoke loudly enough for the entire audience to hear.

    Needs improvement   Satisfactory   Excellent

10. The speaker's words were clear and could be understood.

    Needs improvement   Satisfactory   Excellent

The best part of this presentation was:

_____

_____

_____

_____

_____

_____

_____

A suggestion for improvement is:

_____

_____

_____

_____

_____

_____

_____

Name: _____ Date: _____

 **Activity**
17B

Exploring the Life of a Poet

Directions: Write a brief sketch of the life of the poet you are investigating, and then respond to the questions that follow.

1. Write a brief sketch of the life of the poet.

_____

_____

_____

_____

_____

_____

_____

_____

2. What poems by this author have you read? In what ways do you see his or her life experiences reflected in his or her poetry?

_____

_____

_____

_____

_____

_____

_____

3. Has your understanding of the poet's work changed since you learned more about the poet's life? Why or why not?

_____

_____

_____

_____

_____

_____

_____

_____

4. Do you think that one must understand an author's personal point of view and life experiences in order to understand his or her work? Explain.

_____

_____

_____

_____

_____

_____

_____

_____

Name: _____ Date: _____

 **Activity**
17C

History and Poetry

Directions: Explore the historical context for the life of one of the writers you have read in this unit. Using the chart below, create a timeline showing major historical events and what was happening in the writer's life at that time, including works that he or she was writing. Then respond to the prompt that follows.

Writer:_____

Date(s)	Historical Event	Happenings in the Life of the Writer

In what ways did historical events affect the life and work of the writer?

_____

_____

_____

_____

_____

_____

_____

_____

_____

_____

_____

_____

_____

_____

_____

_____

_____

_____

Name: _____ Date: _____

Self-Review of Writing

Assignment: _____

Directions: Review your writing carefully. For each sentence, circle the choice that best describes your writing. Then complete the two sentences.

1. My main idea is clear.
   Needs improvement   Satisfactory   Excellent

2. My details support the main idea.
   Needs improvement   Satisfactory   Excellent

3. My ideas flow smoothly and in an orderly way.
   Needs improvement   Satisfactory   Excellent

4. The structure clearly follows the Hamburger Model (introduction, body, conclusion).
   Needs improvement   Satisfactory   Excellent

5. My vocabulary is rich and varied.
   Needs improvement   Satisfactory   Excellent

My writing is strong in these ways:

_____

_____

_____

My writing could be improved in these ways:

_____

_____

_____

Name: _____ Date: _____

Activity
18B

Peer Review of Writing

Writer: _____ Assignment: _____

Directions: Read your partner's writing carefully. For each sentence, circle the choice that best describes the writing. Then complete the two sentences.

1. The main idea is clear.
   Needs improvement   Satisfactory   Excellent

2. The details support the main idea.
   Needs improvement   Satisfactory   Excellent

3. The ideas flow smoothly and in an orderly way.
   Needs improvement   Satisfactory   Excellent

4. The structure clearly follows the Hamburger Model (introduction, body, conclusion).
   Needs improvement   Satisfactory   Excellent

5. The vocabulary is rich and varied.
   Needs improvement   Satisfactory   Excellent

The writing is strong in these ways:

_____

_____

_____

The writing could be improved in these ways:

_____

_____

_____

Name: _____ Date: _____

Research Project Evaluation Form

Directions: Use the form to evaluate each component of the research project.

	Needs Improvement	Satisfactory	Excellent
1. The issue and problem are clearly defined.	1	2	3
2. Sources are diverse.	1	2	3
3. Literature sources are summarized.	1	2	3
4. Interview or survey questions are included.	1	2	3
5. Interviews and/or surveys are summarized.	1	2	3
6. Results are reported appropriately.	1	2	3
7. The interpretation of the data is appropriate.	1	2	3
8. Implications of the data are described.	1	2	3
9. Reasonable conclusions are stated.	1	2	3
10. The project paper is mechanically correct.	1	2	3

Strengths of the project:

_____

_____

_____

_____

_____

_____

_____

_____

Areas for improvement:

_____

_____

_____

_____

_____

_____

_____

_____

_____

Compare and Contrast
Mary and Colin

Activity
18D

Directions: Complete the Venn diagram to compare and contrast Mary Lennox and Colin Craven in *The Secret Garden*.

Mary   **Both**   **Colin**

Compare and Contrast Mary and Another Character

Activity 19A

Directions: Complete the Venn diagram to compare and contrast Mary Lennox in *The Secret Garden* and the main character of your choice novel.

Mary   **Both**   _____

Name: _____ Date: _____

 **Activity**
19B

Directions: Complete the Concept Web about growth based on your discussion of its relationship with change. Use examples from *The Secret Garden* and the choice novels.

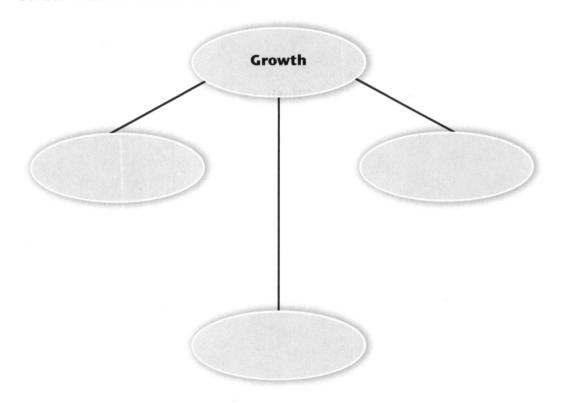

Growth

Literary Reflections · Lesson 19 · Unit Novel Summary

Name: _____ Date: _____

Change Model

Directions: List three or more examples from the novels for each of the following generalizations about change.

Change

Change is linked to time.

_____
_____
_____

Change is everywhere.

_____
_____
_____

Change may be positive or negative.

_____
_____
_____

Change may be perceived as orderly or random.

_____
_____
_____

Change may happen naturally or may be caused by people.

_____
_____
_____

Name: _____ Date: _____

 **Activity**
19D

Hamburger Model

Directions: Use the Hamburger Model to plan a paragraph either
defending the actual title of your choice novel or explaining why the new
title you wrote is a good one.

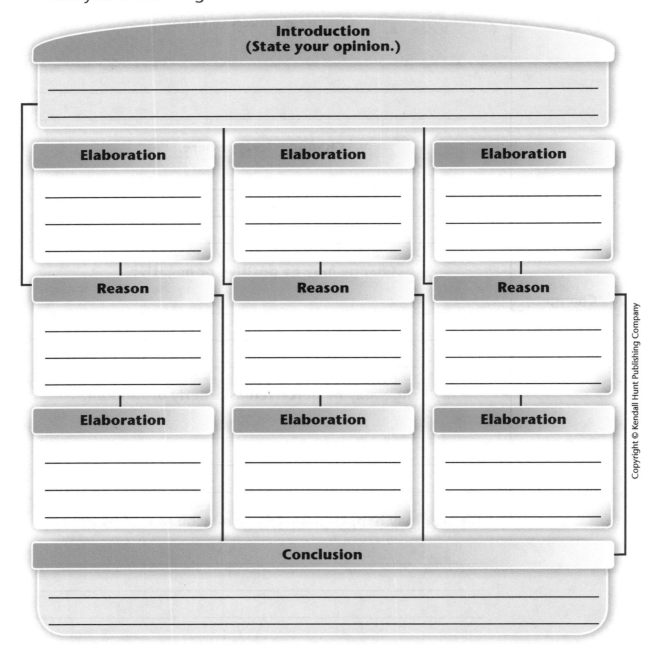

**Introduction
(State your opinion.)**

_____

_____

Elaboration

_____

_____

_____

Elaboration

_____

_____

_____

Elaboration

_____

_____

_____

Reason

_____

_____

_____

Reason

_____

_____

_____

Reason

_____

_____

_____

Elaboration

_____

_____

_____

Elaboration

_____

_____

_____

Elaboration

_____

_____

_____

Conclusion

_____

_____

Vocabulary Web

Activity 20A

Directions: Complete the Vocabulary Web for the word *mood*.

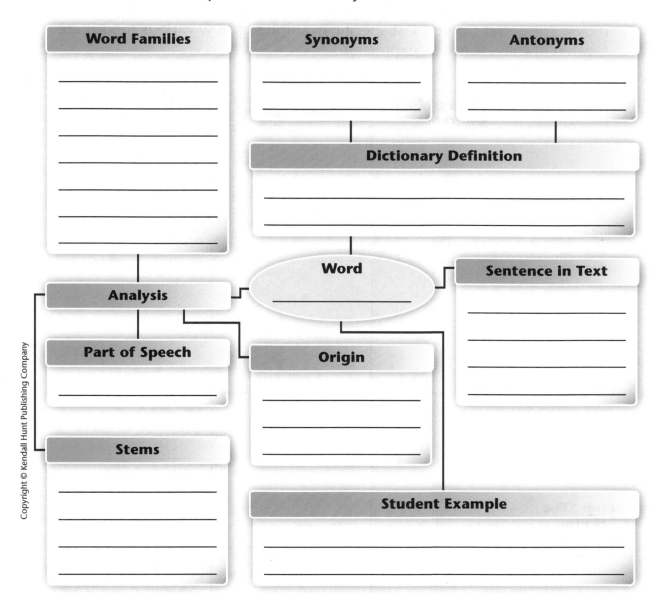

Word Families

_____
_____
_____
_____
_____
_____
_____

Synonyms

_____
_____

Antonyms

_____
_____

Dictionary Definition

_____
_____

Word

_____

Analysis

Part of Speech

_____

Origin

_____
_____
_____

Sentence in Text

_____
_____
_____
_____

Stems

_____
_____
_____
_____

Student Example

_____
_____

Name: _____ Date: _____

 **Activity 20B**

Moods in Literature, Music, and Movies

Directions: Consider parts of the novel *The Secret Garden,* songs from the Broadway soundtrack of *The Secret Garden,* and scenes from the movie *The Secret Garden.* List specific examples of how various moods are created in these forms of expression.

	Text/Song/Movie Reference	Mood Created	How Mood Was Created
Novel			
Song: "The House Upon the Hill"			

	Text/Song/Movie Reference	Mood Created	How Mood Was Created
Song: "Wick"			
Movie			

Name: _____ Date: _____

 **Activity 20C**

Songs from Your Choice Novel

Directions: Complete the chart with events from your choice novel that you believe would make good songs. Record the titles of those songs in the third column.

Title of Choice Novel: _____

Event in Novel	Text Reference	Song Title

Literary Reflections · Lesson 20 · The Secret Garden *in Music*

Choice Novel Project

Directions: In the space provided, complete one of the following projects for your choice novel:

- Write the lyrics (and/or music) of one song for your choice novel.
- Draw the set design for one scene in the novel.
- Draw costumes for several of the novel's characters.
- Write (and/or act out) one scene from your choice novel.

Title of Choice Novel: _____

Name of Project: _____

Name: _____ Date: _____

Oral Presentation
Peer Evaluation

**Activity
21A**

Speaker: _____ Assignment: _____

Directions: For items 1–10, circle the choice that best describes the presentation. Then complete the two sentences.

Content

1. The purpose of the presentation was clear.
   Needs improvement   Satisfactory   Excellent

2. The speaker included details that supported the main idea.
   Needs improvement   Satisfactory   Excellent

3. The speaker showed knowledge of the subject.
   Needs improvement   Satisfactory   Excellent

4. The speaker used vocabulary that was rich, varied, and persuasive.
   Needs improvement   Satisfactory   Excellent

Organization

5. The speech followed the Hamburger Model, with a clear introduction, body, and conclusion.
   Needs improvement   Satisfactory   Excellent

6. The ideas flowed smoothly and in an orderly way.
   Needs improvement   Satisfactory   Excellent

7. The speaker closed the presentation with a strong, interesting idea that restated the purpose.
   Needs improvement   Satisfactory   Excellent

Delivery

8. The speaker made good eye contact with the audience.

Needs improvement   Satisfactory   Excellent

9. The volume of the presentation was adequate.

Needs improvement   Satisfactory   Excellent

10. The speaker's words were clear and could be understood.

Needs improvement   Satisfactory   Excellent

The best part of this presentation was:

_____

_____

_____

_____

_____

_____

_____

A suggestion for improvement is:

_____

_____

_____

_____

_____

_____

_____

Name: _____ Date: _____

Oral Presentation
Teacher Evaluation

Activity
21B

Assignment: _____

Directions: For items 1–10, circle the choice that best describes the presentation. Then complete the two sentences.

Content

1. The purpose of the presentation was clear.
   Needs improvement   Satisfactory   Excellent

2. The speaker included details that supported the main idea.
   Needs improvement   Satisfactory   Excellent

3. The speaker showed knowledge of the subject.
   Needs improvement   Satisfactory   Excellent

4. The speaker used vocabulary that was rich, varied, and persuasive.
   Needs improvement   Satisfactory   Excellent

Organization

5. The speech followed the Hamburger Model, with a clear introduction, body, and conclusion.
   Needs improvement   Satisfactory   Excellent

6. The ideas flowed smoothly and in an orderly way.
   Needs improvement   Satisfactory   Excellent

7. The speaker closed the presentation with a strong, interesting idea that restated the purpose.
   Needs improvement   Satisfactory   Excellent

Delivery

8. The speaker made good eye contact with the audience.

Needs improvement   Satisfactory   Excellent

9. The volume of the presentation was adequate.

Needs improvement   Satisfactory   Excellent

10. The speaker's words were clear and could be understood.

Needs improvement   Satisfactory   Excellent

The best part of this presentation was:

_____

_____

_____

_____

_____

_____

_____

A suggestion for improvement is:

_____

_____

_____

_____

_____

_____

Name: _____ Date: _____

Oral Presentation
Self-Evaluation

Assignment:_____

Directions: For items 1–10, circle the choice that best describes your presentation. Then complete the two sentences.

Content

1. The purpose of my presentation was clear.
   Needs improvement   Satisfactory   Excellent

2. I included details that supported my main idea.
   Needs improvement   Satisfactory   Excellent

3. I showed knowledge of the subject.
   Needs improvement   Satisfactory   Excellent

4. I used vocabulary that was rich, varied, and persuasive.
   Needs improvement   Satisfactory   Excellent

Organization

5. My speech followed the Hamburger Model, with a clear introduction, body, and conclusion.
   Needs improvement   Satisfactory   Excellent

6. My ideas flowed smoothly and in an orderly way.
   Needs improvement   Satisfactory   Excellent

7. I closed the presentation with a strong, interesting idea that restated the purpose.
   Needs improvement   Satisfactory   Excellent

Delivery

8. I made good eye contact with the audience.

Needs improvement   Satisfactory   Excellent

9. The volume of my presentation was adequate.

Needs improvement   Satisfactory   Excellent

10. My words were clear and could be understood by the audience.

Needs improvement   Satisfactory   Excellent

The best part of my presentation was:

_____

_____

_____

_____

_____

_____

_____

A way I could improve is:

_____

_____

_____

_____

_____

_____

_____

Name: _____ Date: _____

Hamburger Model Paragraph Structure

Directions: Use the Hamburger Model structure to organize your ideas about the educational issue.

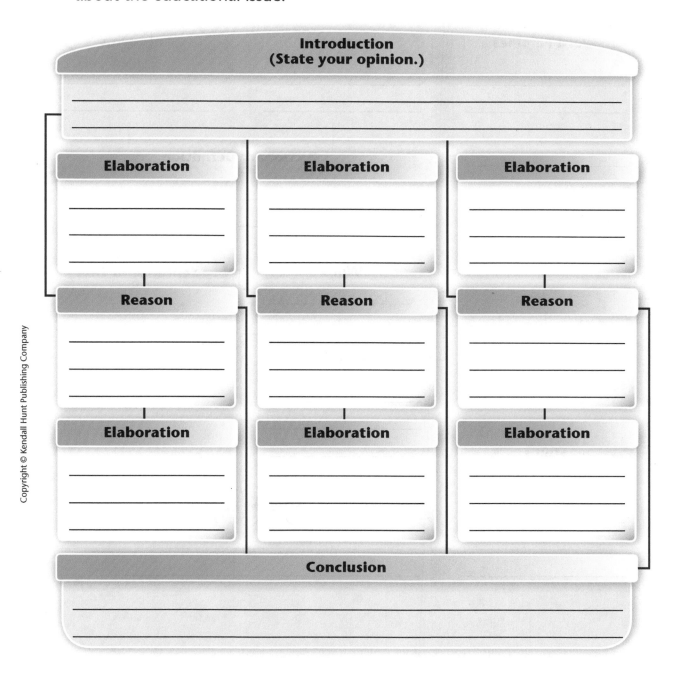

Introduction
(State your opinion.)

Elaboration

Elaboration

Elaboration

Reason

Reason

Reason

Elaboration

Elaboration

Elaboration

Conclusion

Name: _____ Date: _____

Activity 22B

Vocabulary Web

Directions: Complete the Vocabulary Web for an interesting word from your choice novel.

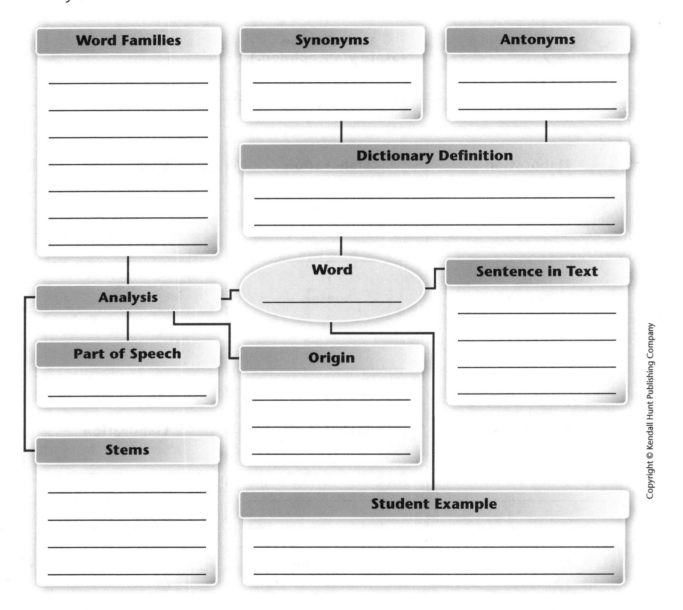

Word Families
_____
_____
_____
_____
_____
_____
_____

Synonyms
_____
_____

Antonyms
_____
_____

Dictionary Definition
_____
_____

Analysis

Word
_____

Sentence in Text
_____
_____
_____

Part of Speech
_____

Origin
_____
_____
_____

Stems
_____
_____
_____
_____

Student Example
_____
_____

Name: _____ Date: _____

Concept Web

Directions: In your group, complete this Concept Web about one of the big ideas of the unit that your group identified. Write the name of the big idea in the top oval. Make additions to the web with information from the unit readings.

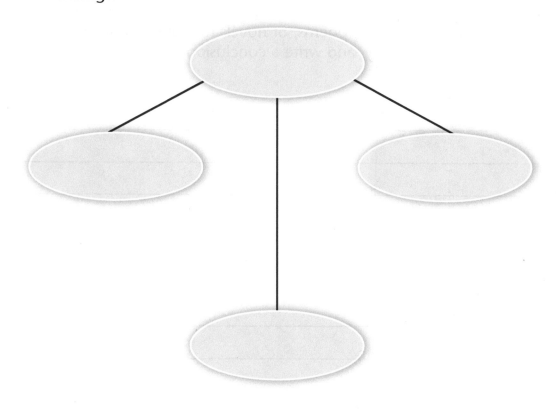

Name: _____ Date: _____

Activity
23B
Final Writing Assignment

Directions: Think about how the literature selections you have read in this unit have reflected the five generalizations about change. Select two generalizations that seemed especially true to you in the unit readings. Write a persuasive essay arguing that the two generalizations are true, using specific examples from the literature to support your points. Use at least four different stories, poems, or novels for your examples. Explain your reasons thoroughly, and write a conclusion to end your essay.

_____

_____

_____

_____

_____

_____

_____

_____

_____

_____

_____

_____

_____

_____

Name: _____ Date: _____

Activity 23C

Change Chart

Directions: Complete this chart with ideas about how the given activities have changed since your parents were your age and how they might change in the future when you have kids of your own. Then write a persuasive essay arguing whether the change you identified is positive or negative. Use the Hamburger Model structure to organize your essay.

	In the Past	**In the Present**	**In the Future**
Using Computers			
Watching Movies			
Watching TV			
Listening to Music			
Driving a Car			

Poor People

Leo Tolstoy

In a small fisherman's cabin, near the edge of the sea, Zhanna, a fisherman's wife, sat by the fire mending an old sail. It was dark and cold outside. The wind was howling. There was a storm over the sea. But in the cabin it was warm and cozy. The earthen floor had been swept clean and a comforting fire was spluttering and hissing softly in the fireplace. Five young children were asleep on a wide bed in the corner.

Zhanna's husband had put out to sea early that morning and had not yet returned. She kept listening to the drone of the waves and the fury of the wind. She was worried.

The old wooden clock struck ten—then eleven, and still he did not return. Zhanna thought of her fisherman husband—how he didn't spare himself and would stay out fishing in cold weather and in storms. She, too, worked from morning till night. But they never had enough to eat. The children didn't have shoes and went about barefoot both in winter and in summer. Zhanna was grateful though that they were strong and healthy. Then she thought of her husband again and she said to herself, "Where is he now? May the Lord watch over him!"

It was too early to go to bed. She put down her sewing, wrapped herself in a heavy shawl, lit a lantern, and went outside to see if the sea was calming down, whether the beacon was still burning in the lighthouse, and if she could see her husband's boat coming in. But she saw nothing in the black darkness.

Zhanna remembered that she had intended to visit her neighbor, the widow, who was very poor and ill and had two small children to care for. Life had been very hard for this woman. "I'll go and stay with her for a while," Zhanna thought.

She approached her neighbor's hut and knocked. There was no answer. Zhanna pushed the door open and entered. It was damp, cold, and dark inside. She raised the lantern to see where the sick woman was. She saw her lying on a small bed that stood right across from the door. The woman was lying very quietly, her head was tilted way back. She did not move at all. Her face was as white as the pillow, and her arm hung limply from the side of the bed.

And on the same bed, near the dead mother, two little children were sleeping. They were curly haired and chubby. They had been covered carefully with the mother's threadbare shawl and with her dress. Evidently the dying woman had tried to care for her young ones to the very last moment of her ebbing life. The children were breathing easily and sleeping peacefully.

Zhanna wrapped the children in her shawl and took them home with her. She put the sleeping orphans near her own children and drew the curtain across the bed.

She was pale and shaken. "What will her husband say? After all, they had five children of their own and a lot of care they were. Why did she bring the others!" Zhanna sat there, at the bed, for a long time, worrying.

It finally stopped raining and it was getting light outside, but the wind continued to howl. Suddenly the door to the cabin was opened, a stream of cold sea air blew into the room and a tall dark-skinned man entered.

"It's me, Zhanna," her husband said.

"Oh, it's you! Thank God!" Zhanna said but she didn't dare look him in the face.

"The weather was awful," he continued. "I hardly caught anything and the nets got torn. I was lucky to get back alive. And what did you do while I was away?"

"I? ..." she began, and grew paler. "I sat here sewing. It was scary. I worried about you."

They were silent for a while.

"Our neighbor the widow, died! Death was not easy for her. How her heart must have ached for her two little ones ..."

Zhanna said no more. Her husband frowned. Then his face grew thoughtful and he looked troubled. After a while he said:

"We'll have to take them in. We'll manage to survive— somehow. Hurry and get them."

But Zhanna did not move.

"Why don't you go? Don't you want to take them in? What's wrong with you, Zhanna?"

"Here they are. I've already brought them," Zhanna said, parting the bed curtain.

Unit Self-Assessment

**Activity
24A**

Directions: For items 1–24, circle the choice that best describes your progress on each of the unit goals. Then respond to the prompts at the end of the assessment.

Goal 1—Interpretation of Literature

1. Literature Preassessment

Needs improvement   Satisfactory   Excellent

2. Literature Webs

Needs improvement   Satisfactory   Excellent

3. Quality of literature discussion

Needs improvement   Satisfactory   Excellent

4. Literature Postassessment

Needs improvement   Satisfactory   Excellent

Goal 2—Writing

5. Persuasive Writing Preassessment

Needs improvement   Satisfactory   Excellent

6. Persuasive writing

Needs improvement   Satisfactory   Excellent

7. Literary response writings

Needs improvement   Satisfactory   Excellent

8. Writing assignment about animals in zoos

Needs improvement   Satisfactory   Excellent

9. *The Secret Garden* writing assignment

Needs improvement   Satisfactory   Excellent

10. Persuasive Writing Postassessment

    Needs improvement   Satisfactory   Excellent

Goal 3—Grammar/Vocabulary

11. Grammar Preassessment

    Needs improvement   Satisfactory   Excellent

12. Vocabulary Webs

    Needs improvement   Satisfactory   Excellent

13. Grammar discussions

    Needs improvement   Satisfactory   Excellent

14. Grammar Postassessment

    Needs improvement   Satisfactory   Excellent

Goal 4—Listening/Speaking

15. Small/large group discussion

    Needs improvement   Satisfactory   Excellent

16. Presentation on dress code (Lesson 14)

    Needs improvement   Satisfactory   Excellent

17. Presentation on title for Emily Dickinson poem (Lesson 17)

    Needs improvement   Satisfactory   Excellent

18. Presentation on research issue (Lesson 21)

    Needs improvement   Satisfactory   Excellent

Goal 5—Reasoning

19. Issue charts

    Needs improvement   Satisfactory   Excellent

20. Discussion/application of Elements and Standards of Reasoning

    Needs improvement   Satisfactory   Excellent

Goal 6—Change

21. Unit Change Matrix

Needs improvement   Satisfactory   Excellent

22. Change Matrix for Novels

Needs improvement   Satisfactory   Excellent

23. Final writing assignment on change (Lesson 23)

Needs improvement   Satisfactory   Excellent

Major Projects

24. Research project on significant issue

Needs improvement   Satisfactory   Excellent

Briefly comment on your progress in understanding the concept of change.

_____

_____

_____

_____

_____

_____

Briefly comment on your progress in the ability to reason.

_____

_____

_____

_____

_____

Inspecting Our Own Ideas: Student Grammar Study

By Michael C. Thompson

As you begin to read this short study of grammar and to think about the ideas you will find here, you should know that there is one important purpose for what you are doing. It is not to learn a large number of facts, or to memorize terms, or to score points. Lots of grammar books can help you learn facts and terms. This study is different. Its purpose is to show you the deeper meaning of grammar that is usually missing from the grammar fact books—the part that many people never understand.

What is this deeper meaning?

It is that grammar is a kind of magic lens, a secret thinking method we can use to peek inside our own minds and to detect the designs of our own ideas.

Using grammar this way, we can learn about ourselves, learn about what makes us human, learn about why some ideas are clear and others are confused, learn about beautiful ways to share our thoughts with other people.

In order to make the most of what you will read, you should understand from the beginning that, even though there will be facts and details to learn, the facts are not the point. The point is the point. And so as you read, do what the coaches always tell you: keep your eye on the ball.

Do not forget that you are concentrating on the deep thinking, the deep meaning, the ability to appreciate the real power of grammar.

The best way to do this is to begin by previewing the study with your teacher. Look over it together, and agree on how much you should read in your first session. Then go read, and think, and reread. Make notes on your ideas and on the questions you have that the reading doesn't answer. Then meet with your teacher to talk about what you have learned and to look over any of the written exercises you may have done. Keep working in this way until you have read the entire grammar study and can discuss it completely with your teacher or other students, depending upon your class situation.

Remember that grammar is a kind of higher order thinking, like logic or mathematics. Grammar can show us secrets that no other thinking method can show us. If you read and think carefully, you will never forget that grammar is a wonderful tool for the mind.

Ideas, Language, and Grammar

How do we talk to each other?

How do we write to each other?

How do we read what someone else has written?

We use **language**. Language is our way of putting words together to make our **ideas**.

Any time we use words to say *something about something*, that is an idea!

We have to say *something . . . about something*.

In other words, an idea is made of *two parts*. One part is *what we are talking about*, and the other part is *what we are saying about it*.

We might say something about ourselves. Or we might say something about an object, such as a distant spiral galaxy in deep space, or a glowing hologram, or a thundering Triceratops. We might say something about wispy, white, cirrostratus clouds in a blue, summer sky. If we did that, we might say: "Wispy, white, cirrostratus clouds in a blue, summer sky floated high over my head."

Do you see the two parts of that idea?

What we are talking about:

Wispy, white, cirrostratus clouds in a blue, summer sky

What we are saying about it:

floated high over my head.

In this idea, we are using words in language to make an idea about cirrostratus clouds.

Of course, if wispy, white clouds in a blue, summer sky floated high over our heads, there would probably be a bird—high, high up—flying near the cloud. This would be a strong bird indeed, since cirrostratus clouds are found at 20,000 feet and higher! There would probably be summer insects buzzing around, eating fresh leaves and drinking nectar from the flowers. The grass would probably be cool and feel good on our bare feet. It would be nice.

Let's get back to language and ideas. Another idea could be, "I'm nobody." In this idea, we are saying something about something. Part one: we are talking about ourselves. Part two: what are we saying about ourselves? That we are nobody. Of course, this idea comes from a very famous poem by

Emily Dickinson, one of America's very greatest poets. And when she said "I'm nobody," she was using irony to change the meaning from bad to good! If you read the rest of the poem, you will see how quickly Emily Dickinson accomplishes this change of meaning.

So, ideas have two parts.

Guess what? We have a very special way to study ideas that we make out of words in language. This special way to study language is called grammar.

Grammar Is a Way of Thinking about Language.

Using grammar, we can inspect one of our own language ideas, and see how language is made! We can do lots of things with grammar. We can find an idea's two parts, and we can find all of the groups of words in the idea, and we can even look at each word by itself and see what it does to make the idea work. This helps us to understand ourselves, and to understand how we think! In the pages that follow, you will learn about grammar, and about how grammar helps us to understand our own ideas.

Review

Let's look again at the ideas we have discussed. Think carefully about each of these points:

Language: Our way of putting words together to express our ideas.

Idea: A two-part thought about something.

The two parts of an idea: What we are talking about, and what we are saying about it.

Grammar: A special way of thinking about language.

Sentence: A Subject and Its Predicate

In grammar, we have a special word to describe an idea that is made of two parts. This special word is **sentence**. A sentence is an idea. We sometimes say that a sentence is a **complete thought**, but this is just a different way of saying the same thing—that a sentence is an idea.

Would you like to know an interesting fact? Our English word *sentence* comes from a very old word, *sententia*, which was a word used thousands of years ago in an ancient language called *Latin*. Latin was the language spoken by the ancient Romans of Italy. To the ancient Romans, the word *sententia* meant "way of thinking." Latin was also the source of our English word *cirrostratus*, which we saw in the first section of this discussion. The word *cirrostratus* comes from the Latin stems *cirrus*, meaning "curl," and *stratus*, meaning "layer." Cirrostratus clouds form a thin, "curly layer" of clouds. We will see that many of the words used in grammar have very logical meanings that are based on ancient Latin or Greek words.

Now, we learned that a sentence is an idea that is complete. But what makes a sentence's idea complete?

It is complete because it has both of the two parts that it needs to make sense to someone. Until it has both of these two important parts, it is not finished, not complete.

Let's think about this for a minute. If I wish to understand you, then there are two things that I need to know:

1. I need to know what you are *talking about*, and

2. I need to know *what you are saying about it*.

If I do know these two things, then I can understand you. If, however, I do not know what you are talking about, or if I do not know what you are saying about it, then I will not understand you.

Grammar gives us names for these two parts of the sentence. The first part of the sentence, what it is about, is called the **complete subject**. The second part of the sentence, what we are saying about the subject, is called the **complete predicate**. Let's look at some examples:

Complete Subject	**Complete Predicate**
(What the idea is about)	(What we are saying about the subject)
The crane	fishes patiently in the lake.
They	would banish us.
The people	could fly.
Crick and Watson	discovered DNA.
I	loved my friend.
Lenny	is a boy in my class.
That day	was one of the coldest.
He	had several beds of zinnias.
She	had a little thin face.
I	am

Notice that a sentence does not have to be long. Sometimes a sentence only has two words in it. "Pterodactyls landed" is a sentence. Even though it is short, it has a subject, *Pterodactyls*, and a predicate, *landed*.

Do you know what pterodactyls were? They were flying dinosaurs that had wings of skin, and that became extinct at the end of the Mesozoic era. In Arizona fossil pterodactyls have been found that had 40-foot wingspans. They are called *pterodactyls* because they had clawed fingers in the middle of their wings, and so their scientific name comes from the ancient Greek *pter*, which means wing, and *dactyl*, which means finger. A second question: Do you know what the Mesozoic era was? Well, *meso* means middle, and *zo* means animal. The Mesozoic era was a geologic era in the earth's history that occurred after the Paleozoic era and before the Cenozoic era, from 230,000,000 years ago until 65,000,000 years ago. The Mesozoic era featured the rise and fall of the dinosaurs and the appearance of birds, grasses, and flowering plants. If you are really adventurous, you will go look up the Paleozoic era, and see what happened then!

Now, let's make some new sentences! I will give you a subject or predicate to start with, and then you can think of your own way to finish the sentence. Sometimes I will give you a subject and leave the predicate blank, and sometimes I will give you a predicate and leave the subject blank. Fill in the blanks with subjects or predicates that help the sentence make sense. For example, if I give you a subject, such as "The star cruiser," you could fill in the

Literary Reflections · Student Grammar Study

predicate blank with a predicate that you imagine. You might complete the sentence by writing, "rumbled toward the icy planet." (Of course, nothing *rumbles* in space, since sound does not carry in a vacuum.)

New Sentences

Complete Subject (What the idea is about)	**Complete Predicate** (What we are saying about the subject)
1. F. L. Wright, the famous architect,	_____
2. Egyptian hieroglyphics	_____
3. The red laser beam	_____
4. _____	shone across the Mediterranean.
5. _____	quietly munched the bamboo shoots.
6. _____	climbed aboard the Hispaniola.
7. The people of ancient Carthage	_____
8. Beethoven's best symphony	_____
9. _____	is my favorite work of art.
10. _____	littered the laboratory.

Notice that until you completed the subject or predicate, none of your sentences made sense. A subject or a predicate by itself is not an idea; it is only a fragment, or piece of an idea. A sentence fragment is a piece of a sentence that only makes an incomplete thought. A sentence fragment needs to be finished, just like the subjects and predicates above needed to be finished.

How would I have finished the ten sentences you just worked on? Well, I might have finished them this way:

Complete Subject (What the idea is about)	**Complete Predicate** (What we are saying about the subject)
1. F. L. Wright, the famous architect,	*designed houses to match the landscape.*
2. Egyptian hieroglyphics	*are made of little pictures.*
3. The red laser beam	*could be seen from the moon.*
4. *The ship's festive lights*	shone across the Mediterranean.
5. *The panda bear*	quietly munched the bamboo shoots.
6. *The wide-eyed, young boy*	climbed aboard the Hispaniola.

7. The people of ancient Carthage   *waved good-bye to Hannibal.*

8. Beethoven's best symphony   *is a musical masterpiece.*

9. *Van Gogh's self-portrait*   is my favorite work of art.

10. *Empty pizza boxes*   littered the laboratory.

By the way, the *Hispaniola* was the sailing ship in Robert Louis Stevenson's wonderful classic, *Treasure Island*, which is about young Jim Hawkins and his adventures with the dastardly pirates led by Long John Silver. If you have not read this masterpiece, you are in for a great time. I know you would enjoy looking up the famous architect, Frank Lloyd Wright (find photographs of his buildings), as well as the ancient general Hannibal, the great composer Ludwig van Beethoven (listen to a recording of his famous Fifth Symphony), and the Dutch painter Vincent Van Gogh (look at a reproduction of his painting *Starry Night*).

Now you can make up some sentences of your own. Write the subjects in the blanks at the left, and write the predicates in the blanks at the right. Use your creativity and imagination to write some unexpected and interesting sentences.

Sentences

Complete Subject
(What the idea is **about**)

1. _____

2. _____

3. _____

Complete Predicate
(What **we are saying** about the subject)

1. _____

2. _____

3. _____

Review

Now let's look again at the new ideas we have learned about language and sentences.

Our way of putting words together to make our ideas is called **language**.

A two-part thought about something is called an **idea**.

What we are talking about and what we are saying about it are the **two parts of an idea**.

A special way of thinking about language is called **grammar**.

In grammar, we call a two-part idea a **sentence**.

The two parts of the sentence are called the **subject** and the **predicate**.

What the sentence is about is called the **subject**.

What we are saying about the subject is called the **predicate**.

A piece of a sentence that is not complete is only a **fragment**.

What Is a Sentence Like?

Now that you understand that a sentence is made of two parts—a subject the sentence is about and a predicate that says something about the subject—think of some other things that also have two parts. For example, an egg has both a white and a yolk inside. A basketball goal has a backboard and a rim. A bicycle wheel has a center and a rim. A person has a first name and a last name. Make a list of things that, like sentences, have two parts. After my first examples, fill in your own.

The Thing	Part One	Part Two
egg	white	yolk
mouth	upper lip	lower lip
shooting an arrow	pull back	let go
echo	sound goes away	sound comes back
_____	_____	_____
_____	_____	_____
_____	_____	_____
_____	_____	_____
_____	_____	_____
_____	_____	_____
_____	_____	_____

Now that you have a list of things that have two parts, which one of these things in your list do you think is really most like a sentence, with its two subject/predicate parts? What is the best comparison? Think about it carefully, and then explain your choice:

Did you enjoy thinking that way? Thinking up comparisons between two different things is a special and important kind of thinking, called *synthesis*. Synthesis is the ability to see connections, or similarities, or relationships between things that seem unconnected at first. When we use synthesis to see hidden connections, we are often surprised to learn how similar things are, and how much everything is connected.

A vocabulary note: The word *subject* contains two ancient Latin word pieces, or stems, that we see in many words, *sub* and *ject*. The stem *sub* means "under," and we see *sub* in words such as *submarine* and *submerge*. The stem *ject* means "throw," and we see *ject* in words such as *eject* and *dejected*. So the word *subject* actually contains a picture: the *subject* of a sentence is the part that is "thrown down" for discussion. Look up some of the following example words in your dictionary, and see if you can understand why they mean what they mean:

Stem	Meaning	Example Words
sub	under	submarine, submerge, subdue, subtract, subside, subordinate
ject	throw	reject, dejected, interject, eject, conjecture, project, adjective, object

Clauses: The Sentences Within Sentences

There is another surprising fact about the way we make our ideas into sentences. Many of the sentences that we use are just like the ones we have already studied. They have a subject, and then a predicate, and then the sentence ends. Sometimes, however, our ideas get so connected that we like to join simple ideas together into a longer, more complicated idea. In other words, sometimes, we join little related sentences together into a big sentence. For example, we might have these two sentences:

Congress passed the bill. The president signed it into law.

Each of these sentences has its own subject and predicate. But since these two sentences describe something that happened in a connected event, we can connect the sentences together into a longer sentence:

Congress passed the bill, and the president signed it into law.

Now the two little sentences make one long sentence, and it has one subject and predicate, followed by a second subject and predicate, all in one sentence!

<u>Congress</u>   <u>passed the bill,</u> and <u>the president</u>   <u>signed it into law.</u>
  subject   predicate   subject   predicate

When we join little sentences this way into a longer sentence of subject/predicate chains, we call each little subject/predicate group a clause.

<u>Congress passed the bill,</u>   and   <u>the president signed it into law.</u>
     first clause   second clause

When there is only one subject/predicate set in the sentence, we say that the sentence has one **clause.**

Our word clause comes from the ancient Latin word *claudere*, which meant "to close" to the Romans. This makes sense even now because a clause is a group of words in which an idea gets opened, and closed! The idea is opened when we introduce a subject, and then it is closed when we provide the predicate. In a long sentence made of many clauses, we open and close a number of related ideas in a row. Let's look at some examples of clauses in sentences. Notice that each clause has its own subject and its own predicate:

Clauses in Sentences

1. <u>Our forefathers</u>   <u>brought forth upon this continent a new nation.</u>
      subject   predicate

_____
a one-clause sentence

2. <u>I</u>   <u>will arise,</u>   and   <u>I</u>   <u>will go now.</u>
subj.   predicate   subj.   predicate

_____   _____
first clause   second clause

_____
a two-clause sentence

3. <u>Robert Frost</u> <u>has miles to go</u> before <u>he</u> <u>sleeps.</u>
   subject   predicate   subj. predicate

_____   _____
first clause   second clause

_____
a two-clause sentence

4. When   <u>the attack</u> <u>finally begins,</u> <u>you</u> <u>sneak up quietly,</u> and
         subject   predicate   subj.   predicate

_____   _____
first clause   second clause

<u>the gang</u> <u>throws balloons.</u>
 subject   predicate

_____
third clause

_____
a three-clause sentence

See? We can make long sentences out of any number of related ideas!

But why is it important to know this?

By using grammar to inspect our own ideas, we have discovered that our wonderful brains can understand ideas and the relationships between different ideas so well and so quickly that we can connect these ideas into sentences of clauses faster than we can even speak. We can do it without even knowing we are doing it, and before we even have a name for it. It is only now, when we use grammar to inspect our ideas, that we begin to realize what powerful things our minds are. The grammar of clauses shows us how our minds build beautiful structures of ideas.

Parts of Speech: The Kinds of Words

One thing you have noticed about all ideas or sentences: every sentence is made of words. A word is a group of sounds or letters that means something. In the sentence, "The famous author Robert Louis Stevenson (1850–1894) wrote the novel, Treasure Island," there are 11 words. For example, Robert is a word and the is a word. We always put blank spaces between words in a written sentence. If you look at a college dictionary, you will see that we have many thousands of words in our language. In fact, there are far more words than anyone could ever learn!

Just imagine that you traveled to a land far, far away.

(One faraway land is Nepal, near Tibet in the continent of Asia, where Mount Everest, the highest mountain in the world, is. Mount Everest is 29,028 feet high, and it is in the Himalayan mountain range. It is so high that it has only been climbed a few times. Nepal's high-altitude capital is Katmandu. There is a wonderful novel you will want to read one day, *Lost Horizon*, written by James Hilton in 1933, that depicts Nepal under the fictitious name of "Shangri-La.")

Now, just imagine that you travel to a land far, far away, and the gray-bearded king of the land says, "You may have all of the treasures in my kingdom if you can tell me how many kinds of words there are." The king then looks down to the green valleys far, far below, and an icy wind comes down from the frozen peaks above, and blows through your hair.

What would you say? There are thousands and thousands of words in the dictionary. Are there thousands of kinds of words? Are there hundreds of kinds of words?

Well, you are in luck, because if you set off on an adventure one day, you will be prepared with the knowledge that there are only eight kinds of words! Just imagine! All of those words in the dictionary can be put into only eight piles, and the eight different kinds of words are easy to learn. We call the eight kinds of words the eight **parts of speech** because all of our speech can be *parted* into only eight piles of words.

The names of the eight parts of speech are the *noun, pronoun, adjective, verb, adverb, preposition, conjunction,* and *interjection*. In a sentence, each part of speech has something different to do. And since a sentence might only have two words in it, you can tell that not every sentence uses all eight parts of speech.

The only parts of speech that have to be in a sentence are the noun or pronoun and the verb. Can you guess why? Let's learn about the eight parts of speech and their functions (uses). As you read the following pages, study the definitions, examples, and discussions of the eight parts of speech carefully and slowly.

The Parts of Speech

Part of Speech	Function	Examples
noun (n.)	name of something	*Mary, dog, garden, sound*

A noun is the name of a person, *Picasso*, or the name of a place, *Amsterdam*, or the name of a thing, *aurora*. The sentence "The wind in the willows whispered in the leaves" has three nouns: wind, willows, and leaves. Nouns give us names for things!

Proper nouns are the names of specific people, places, or things. Otherwise, they are common nouns. Study the following examples to see the difference.

Proper Nouns	*Common Nouns*
John	boy
Chicago	city
Statue of Liberty	monument

Nouns can be **singular**, like *dog*, or **plural**, like *dogs*. Proper nouns, like *Istanbul*, are capitalized, but common nouns, like *boy*, are not capitalized.

Part of Speech	Function	Examples
pronoun (pron.)	replaces a noun	*I, she, him, it, them*

A pronoun is a short word that replaces a usually longer noun so that we can speak faster. For example, instead of always saying a person's name, such as *Abraham Lincoln*, in a sentence, we can say *he*. In the sentence "He was born in a log cabin in Illinois," the words *Abraham Lincoln* have been replaced by the short pronoun *he*. Pronouns make language fast!

Two common kinds of pronouns are the **subject pronouns**:

I, you, he, she, it, we, you, they

and the **object pronouns**:

me, you, him, her, it, us, you, them

We have learned that every sentence has a subject and a predicate. Also, every subject contains either a noun or a pronoun. This noun or pronoun that the sentence is about is sometimes called the **simple subject**. The **complete subject** is the simple subject and all the words around it that modify it. Consider the following example:

The big, brown bear lumbered into the woods.

The word *bear* is the simple subject. *The big, brown bear* is the complete subject.

adjective (adj.)	modifies a noun or pronoun	*red, tall, fast, good, the*

To modify is to *change*. An adjective is a word that changes the meaning of a noun or pronoun. For example, for the noun *tree*, we can change it by saying *tall* tree, or *Christmas* tree, or *cherry* tree, and each of these different adjectives changes (we sometimes say *modifies*) the noun and gives us a different picture in our minds. Another example: the noun *garden* could be modified by either the adjective *flower* or the adjective *secret*. We could talk about a *flower* garden, but we could use a different adjective and talk about a *secret* garden instead, and that would modify the idea. Some adjectives are the opposites of one another: a *fast* car is the opposite of a *slow* car.

The most common adjectives are the three little words *a, an,* and *the.* These three adjectives are called the articles. The word *the* is called the **definite article**, and the words *a* and *an* are called the **indefinite articles**.

Notice that the noun, pronoun, and adjective go together and work together. The nouns name things, the pronouns replace the nouns, and the adjectives modify either nouns or pronouns. You could say that the noun, with its supporting pronouns and adjectives, forms a little noun system, like the sun with its planets.

verb (v.)	an action or equals word	*jumps, fell, is*

Every sentence contains a verb, which is sometimes called the **simple predicate**. The **complete predicate** is the simple predicate and all the words around it that modify it. For example:

> The big, brown bear lumbered into the woods.

The word *lumbered* is the simple predicate. *Lumbered into the woods* is the complete predicate.

There are two kinds of verbs.

Action verbs show action: they show people and things doing things. Look at the action verbs in these sentences: the dog *barked.* The tall man *grinned.* My best friend *reads* lots of books. We *drove* to Florida. Mary *opened* her brown eyes.

Linking verbs are equals words. They show that two things are the same. For example, in the sentence "Siegfried is a good student." the verb *is* means that Siegfried and the good student are the same person. Siegfried IS the good student.

Action: Michelangelo ran after the ball.

Linking: Michelangelo is good at soccer.

Action: Donatello drew a sketch.

Linking: Donatello is a genius.

Action: Raphael plays baseball in the spring.

Linking: Raphael is a pitcher on the baseball team.

My favorite linking verb sentence is by the poet Marianne Moore, who said that poems *are* imaginary gardens with real toads in them. Don't you like that idea?

Parts of the sentence: We have learned about two parts of the sentence already, the **simple subject** and the **simple predicate** or verb. Well, there are two other parts of the sentence you can identify if you know what kind of verb you have. When an action verb sentence shows the subject doing something to something, as in the sentence "The dog bit the mailman," we call the noun or pronoun that receives the action a **direct object**. When a linking verb sentence shows that the subject is *equal to* something else, as in the sentence "The dog is a poodle," we call the noun or pronoun that is linked to the subject a **subject complement**.

Direct object: Achilles grabbed the *warrior.*

Subject complement: Achilles was a *warrior.*

Notice that the only way to tell whether the second noun in these sentences is a direct object or a subject complement is to look at the verb. If a sentence contains an action verb, it might have a direct object, but if the sentence contains a linking verb, it might have a subject complement. This is a very advanced grammar idea, and it gives us deep insight into the way we form our own ideas.

Tense: Another very important fact: verbs change, according to the *time* they are describing. The time of the verb is called the verb **tense**. The three most familiar verb tenses are the **present tense**, the **past tense**, and the **future tense**. The verb to *believe*, for example, takes these forms:

Present tense: I *believe* in miracles.

Past tense: I *believed* in miracles.

Future tense: I *will believe* in miracles.

adverb (adv.)   **modifies a verb, adj., or adv.**   *quickly, slowly, well*

An adverb is a word that modifies or changes the meaning of a verb, an adjective, or another adverb.

Adverb modifies verb: I swam *quickly*.

Adverb modifies adverb: I swam *very* quickly.

Adverb modifies adjective: I saw a *very* red star.

Before you continue reading, study these three examples very carefully, and make sure you understand every part of speech in every sentence.

Notice that many adverbs end in *ly*, such as *quickly, slowly, loudly, nearly, badly,* and *hungrily*.

Notice that the verb and adverb form a little system together. Just as the noun is often accompanied by an adjective, the verb is often accompanied by an adverb that gives it new meaning.

Just as adjectives help us adjust the meanings of nouns when the nouns are not quite what we mean, adverbs help us adjust the meanings of verbs. Adjectives and adverbs are modifiers that help us adjust the meanings of nouns and verbs.

preposition (prep.)   **shows relationship**   *in, on, beside, after*

A **preposition** is a word that shows how two things are *related* to each other in space or time. Space examples: The dog was *on* the dock. The book is *in* the drawer. The boy was *inside* the secret garden. The garden was *behind* the wall. Time examples: The movie is *after* the news. My birthday is *before* yours. She got sick *during* the game. Prepositions are little words, but they are very important because they show where everything is in space and time. Prepositions let us make ideas that show how the world is arranged!

Another interesting fact about prepositions is that they are always found in little word groups, such as *in* the box, *on* the dock, *under* the bed, *around* the world, and *over* the rainbow. These little word groups always begin with prepositions, and they are called **prepositional phrases**.

In fact, the word *preposition* is made of the Latin *pre*, which means *before*, and the word *position*. A preposition is called a preposition because its *position is always before* the other words in the prepositional phrase! It has the preposition.

conjunction (conj.)   **joins words**   *and, or, but, so, yet*

A conjunction is a word that joins two other words together into a pair. Michael *and* David ate many hot dogs. By using the conjunction *and*, we can join the two nouns *Michael* and *David* together so we can talk about them both at once, as a pair. We can use a conjunction to join two pronouns: Give the lithograph to him *or* her. If we want to, we can even use a conjunction to join two verbs: Mary thought *and* wondered. We can use a conjunction to join two adverbs: He spoke quickly, *but* confidently. Or we can use a conjunction to join two adjectives: The wall was high *and* dark. Conjunctions let us join things into pairs!

Would you like one more very interesting example? You can even use a conjunction to join two groups of words together. For example, you can use a conjunction to join two prepositional phrases together: The albatross flew over the ship *and* around the mast.

| interjection (interj.) | shows emotion | *Oh, wow, yes, no, well* |

Interjections do not do anything special, such as join words, or modify words, or replace words. All they do is show emotion. If we say, "Wow, you look nice!" the word *wow* just shows happiness or excitement. The most common interjections are the words *yes* and *no*. Another very common interjection is the word *oh*: Oh, yes, I like interjections. Do you?

A Vocabulary Note

The word *preposition* contains two ancient Latin word pieces, or stems, *pre*, and *pos*. We see these stems in many words. The stem *pre* means "before," and we see *pre* in words such as *predict* and *prepare*. The stem *pos* means "put," and we see *pos* in words such as *position* and *depose*. So the word preposition contains a picture: the preposition is the part that is "put before" the other words in the phrase. The word *conjunction* also contains stems that appear in many other words: *con* and *junct*. The stem *con* means "together," and the stem *junct* means "join." In the words *adverb* and *adjective*, we see the stem *ad*, which means "to," and the word *pronoun* contains the stem *pro*, which means "for" or sometimes "forward." Look up some of the following example words in your dictionary, and see if you can understand why they mean what they mean:

Stem	Meaning	Example Words
pre	before	predict, prepare, preliminary, preschool, preface, premonition
pos	put	position, depose, interpose, suppose, deposit, repose
con	together	conjunction, contact, connect, contiguous, contract, converge
junct	join	juncture, disjunction, injunction, adjunct, conjunction
ad	to	adjective, adverb, adherent, adjacent, adapt, admit
pro	for/forward	pronoun, propel, prophet, proponent, prominent, promote

Now, you know that the stem *ject* means "throw." In the word *object*, however, we also see the stem *ob*, which means "toward" or "about." We see the stem *ob* in many words: *object, obstacle, obdurate, oblique, obloquy, objurgate,* and *obscure,* for example. Use your dictionary to look up the full etymology of the word *object* and see if you can understand why we call objects *objects*. Then answer this question: How are direct objects in sentences similar to objects on the ground?

Review

Let's look again at what the eight kinds of words do. Study the parts of speech until you have their functions memorized. Make sure that you can remember some examples of each one.

| **noun** | name of something | Mike, dog, tree, sound |

The *boy* listened to the *music of Verdi.*

Literary Reflections · Student Grammar Study

pronoun	replaces a noun	I, she, him, it, them

She and *I* saw *him* and *her* at the Museum of Modern Art.

adjective	modifies a noun or pronoun	red, tall, fast, good, the

Isaac Newton, *a famous* mathematician, discovered *the natural* law.

verb	an action or equals word	jumps, fell, is

I *lost* the Byron poem yesterday, but I *have* it now.

adverb	modifies a verb	quickly, slowly, well

The pianist played her Chopin solo *beautifully*.

preposition	shows relationship	in, on, beside, after

The government is *of* the people, *by* the people, and *for* the people.

conjunction	joins words	and, or, but

I saw the doctor, *and* she gave me some medicine.

interjection	shows emotion	Oh, wow, yes, no, well

Oh, yes, I always vote in the elections.

Examples

Now let's look at some sentences, and inspect the parts of speech in each one. We will use a little arrow, like this », to show what noun an adjective modifies, or to show what verb an adverb modifies.

```
      adj.  »  n.           v.      adj.  »  n.
1. The architect    designed    a    bridge.
      subject                  predicate
```

Notice that the noun bridge is a direct object of the action verb designed.

          n.   adv.   » v.   adj. » n.

2. **Michelangelo** **carefully** **painted** **the** **ceiling.**
      subject   predicate

Notice that the noun ceiling is a direct object of the action verb painted.

    interj. pron. conj. pron. v.   n.

3. **Yes,** **you** **and** **I** **are** **friends.**
             subject   predicate

Notice that the noun *friends* is a subject complement of the linking verb *are*.

     n.   v.   prep.   adj. » n.

4. **Magellan** **sailed** **around** **the** **planet.**
    subject   predicate

     n.   conj. pron. n.   prep.   n.   v.

5. **Alexander** **and** **his** **army** **of** **Macedonians** **won.**
                subject   predicate

Now, notice some very interesting things about the grammar of these sentences:

- The subject can be one word or many words.
- The predicate can be one word or many words.
- The main word of the subject is always a noun or pronoun.
- The main word of the predicate is always a verb.
- A sentence always contains a noun or pronoun and a verb.

You try it.

Here are some more sentences. Study each one carefully and imitate the five examples just presented by writing the abbreviation for the part of speech above each word, and by underlining the subject and predicate of each sentence. Identify any direct objects or subject complements you see.

1. **The scientist used a microscope.**

2. **Rembrandt slowly painted the canvas.**

3. **Yes, he and she were members.**

4. **De Soto floated down the Mississippi.**

5. **Spartacus and his force of gladiators lost.**

Check your answers against the answer key on the next page.

Answer Key

adj. » n.   v.   adj. » n.

1. **The   scientist   used   a   microscope.**
        subject   predicate

The noun *microscope* is a direct object.

n.   adj.   » v.   adj. » n.

2. **Rembrandt   slowly   painted   the   canvas.**
        subject   predicate

The noun *canvas* is a direct object.

interj. pron. conj. pron.   v.   n.

3. **Yes,   he   and   she   were   members.**
             subject   predicate

The noun *members* is a subject complement.

n.   v.   prep.   adj. » n.

4. **De Soto   floated   down   the   Mississippi.**
       subject   predicate

n.   conj. pron. n.   prep.   n.   v.

5. **Spartacus   and   his   force   of   gladiators   lost.**
                   subject   predicate

(I know, you want to know who Rembrandt, De Soto, and Spartacus were. Well, Rembrandt van Rijn was a Dutch master painter who was born in 1606 and died in 1669. Rembrandt did a self-portrait that is one of the most striking and penetrating in the history of art. Hernando De Soto was a courageous Spanish explorer, born about 1500, who is credited with discovering the Mississippi River, although the American Indians had actually discovered it long, long before any Europeans arrived in the New World. Spartacus was a proud Thracian slave in the Roman Empire who became a gladiator and who led a slave revolt against Rome. Spartacus and his men were annihilated in 71 B.C.)

Now, think about this:

One day, long, long ago, some human being uttered the first word, and language began. Over a period of time, human beings developed language, and more and more parts of speech were created, until there were eight. Use your common sense and imagination to guess what you think was probably the part of speech of the first words ever used. Think about it, and then write down your guess and the reason you think it is probable.

The part of speech of the first word ever used was _____ .

I think this because: _____

_____

_____

_____

_____

_____

_____

_____

_____

_____

Phrases: The Clever Teamwork

We all know what teams are. Five players work together on a basketball team, and each player has his or her own part in executing a well-practiced play. Cheerleaders work together to make a single pyramid, with each cheerleader standing on the shoulders of two cheerleaders below. Lawyers can work as a team to win a single case. Computer programmers work in teams to write programs; each programmer specializes in writing a different part of the computer code.

Well, by inspecting our own ideas with grammar, we have discovered a remarkable thing. Sometimes, a whole group of words will team together to imitate a single part of speech! A team of words acting as a single part of speech is called a **phrase**. We learned a bit about **prepositional phrases** when we studied the parts of speech, but now we are ready to learn more. Here is a more complete definition of the phrase: a *phrase* is a group of words that acts as a single part of speech, and that does not contain a subject and its predicate. For example, notice that a prepositional phrase can behave as though it were an adverb, modifying a verb:

An ordinary adverb: The penguin sat *there*.

A phrase: The penguin sat *on the iceberg*.

In each case, the verb *sat* is being modified by something, but in the first example the verb is being modified by a simple adverb, *there*, whereas in the second example, the verb is being modified by a group of words, *on the iceberg*, acting as a team to make an adverb. That is what phrases are: word groups imitating other parts of speech. It is interesting, by the way, to note that our English word *phrase* comes from a very ancient Greek word, *phrazein*, which meant "to speak."

A prepositional phrase can also act as an adjective:

- An ordinary adjective: The *top* book is a classic.

- A phrase: The book *on the top* is a classic.

There are different kinds of phrases. Let's look at some other phrases, and see some of the interesting forms that phrases can take in sentences. Remember to notice that the phrase never contains both a sentence's subject and its predicate, and that a sentence can contain more than one phrase, or no phrase at all.

Phrases

Carmen, *my favorite opera*, is by the composer Bizet.

Not remembering names is my problem.

Birds fly *over the rainbow*.

I pledge allegiance *to the flag*.

The assault team climbed the north face of *Mount Everest*.

Magellan sailed *around the world*.

Newton loved to *study mathematics*.

The painting *on the museum's north wall* was painted *by the French painter Monet*.

Conclusion

Now, let's think carefully about all of the things that we have learned. We have learned a very important secret about the way we think and express our ideas about the world. The secret is that our **ideas**, which we sometimes call **sentences**, are only complete when they are made of two parts. These two parts are the subject that the sentence is about, and the predicate that says something about the subject. If we do not have both of these parts in our ideas, we will not have a complete thought, and we will not make any sense to anyone else. Other people have to know both of these parts in order to understand our ideas; they have to know what we are talking about, and they have to know what we are saying about it.

We also learned that sometimes simple sentences can be connected together into more complicated ideas, and then we say that each little subject/predicate group inside the long sentence is a **clause**.

We have also learned an amazing secret about the thousands and thousands of words in our English language: there are only eight kinds! We call these eight kinds of words the **parts of speech**. We have learned that each kind of word has a special purpose, a function, in a sentence. Two of the parts of speech, the **noun** and the **verb**, are special, because they are in almost every sentence. The **subject** of a sentence usually has a noun (but it might have a **pronoun** instead to take the noun's place), and the predicate of the sentence always (yes, always) has a verb.

In studying the parts of speech, we learned that they are used as **parts of the sentence**. The **simple subject** is the noun or pronoun that the sentence is about. The **simple predicate** is the subject's verb. The **direct object** is a noun or pronoun that receives the action of the action verb, and the **subject complement** is the noun or pronoun linked to the subject by the linking verb.

We have learned that our minds are clever enough to collect little groups of words together into **phrases** that imitate other parts of speech, and we have seen examples of phrases acting as adverbs, as adjectives, and even as nouns (if you did not notice that, go back and look closely at the examples of phrases).

Finally, **verbs** have taught us a very important secret about ideas. Because there are two kinds of verbs, the **action** kind and the **equals or linking** kind, this means that there are two main kinds of ideas. We can either say that the *subject is doing something*, or we can say that the *subject is something*. For example, we can use an action verb and say, "The reader of this book *saw* a very good student." But if we use a linking/equals verb, we can say something even better: "The reader of this book *is* a very good student."

You Try It

adj.	n.	prep.	adj.	n.	v.	adj.	adv.	adj.	n.
The	**reader**	**of**	**this**	**book**	**is**	**a**	**very**	**good**	**student.**
simple subj.			prep. phrase		simple pred.				subject
									complement

complete subject ———————————— complete predicate

a one-clause sentence

See if you can analyze the following sentence as I analyzed the one above:

We   inspect   ideas   with   grammar.

Check the next page for an analysis of this sentence.

pronoun	verb	noun	prep.	noun
We	**inspect**	**ideas**	**with**	**grammar.**
simple subject	simple predicate	direct object		

_____   _____
subject   complete predicate

_____
a one-clause sentence

The Last Word

As you see, grammar is a fascinating way to think about our own thinking. By using grammar, we can examine our thoughts, and we can see how we have made those thoughts. If we did not have grammar, we would never really be able to understand how powerful our minds are. After this short introduction to grammar, however, you have begun to understand how powerfully your mind makes ideas out of language. As you learn more and more about grammar in the future, you will gain greater insight into how wonderful it is to be a human being, an idea-maker. I hope that you will always look forward to the wonderful study of grammar. It is truly a way of inspecting our own ideas.